The Scientist and Ethical Decision

edited by Charles Hatfield

InterVarsity Press
Downers Grove, Illinois 60515

InterVarsity Press
is the book publishing
division of Inter-Varsity
Christian Fellowship.

"Thy Speech Betrayeth
Thee" by Kenneth L. Pike
is reprinted (on page 79)
from Mark My Words, and
used by permission of
Wm. B. Eerdmans Publishing
Co., Grand Rapids,
Michigan.

ISBN 0-87784-762-2

Library of Congress Catalog
Card Number: 73-84594

Printed in the United
States of America

Contents

Introduction by Charles Hatfield

Introduction by Charles Hatfield

The public image of the scientist is no longer monolithic. If he is Dr. Jekyll to some, he is Mr. Hyde to others.

One reason for this is that the effects of science as they have been worked out in technology have not always been beneficent. The scientist is thus charged with the ecological crisis, the energy crisis, the search for the ultimate weapon, the population explosion, the drug culture and so forth.

The scientist's own problem, however, is that he is like a father attending the birth of his own child (new knowledge). He seems as little able to control its future use as a real father can change the eye color of his own progeny. Yet, if this were really so, then the scientist could not be held responsible. The fact is that the scientist is both a professional (and thus involved in the discovery of new knowledge) and a man. Ethical decisions are therefore his to make, regardless of how little they sometimes affect the use to which his work is put.

Furthermore, when a scientist is also a Christian—and a reflective one at that—there is both a special burden for him and a special reward for culture at large when he speaks out on ethical issues. For a scientist who is a Christian can bring to ethical decisions a perspective which is not limited to the rumblings of his own internal moral conscience. He has at his disposal principles from Scripture, and these, or at least so is the Christian claim, have a transcendent origin. Thus what the scientist who is a Christian thinks about scientific work and ethical decision should be both significant and instructive.

In any case, it is certainly important for our society to avoid what Bertrand de Jouvenel calls "a new fatalism," a feeling "that our future is determined for us by the autonomous course of a super-human agency, whose god-like nature is acknowledged . . . an idol which richly rewards its servants who do not question its course. . . . We prove more naive than the primitives; when they made idols of natural forces, it was at least true that these were outside their control and generated in a manner they could not understand, which is of course not true of Technology. It would be hard to find a phenomenon more dependent upon human decision than the evolution of techniques [technologies]."

We seem slow to learn that human values and human technologies are not on the same level. The moral and ethical must control the technological at the interface of practical use. In words that come with a surprisingly modern ring across the mists of Walden Pond, we must not "become the tools of our tools." Yet that is what has happened. And when technologies are allowed to "run themselves," people are usually hurt. The result is ever the same: Human values are either impaired or destroyed.

In this sense technologies serve a useful purpose as a warning: They have an *M.E.*, or magnification effect. They keep our eyes focused upon the fact that the use of technologies is only the result of a decision by human beings. Nothing we use is automatic unless we decide to design it that way. (M.E. also suggests the *me,* the human component of the decision.) The use and abuse of technologies make it clear that the problem is unavoidably man himself: his value, his meaning and how he conceives his role in the world. We are learning that technological feats must be labeled just that, and that they must never be allowed to usurp control.

The history of decisions regarding the use of science and its "latest" development often uncovers a betrayal of human values, as leaders have too readily opted for short-range benefits rather than long-range wisdom. It is not likely that future historians will be so kind in their evaluation of this era as we might wish. The hour is late, and, while we should be well launched into reasonable solutions, we find ourselves still reviewing the problems.

We *are,* however, slowly building up experience in solving some of the smaller problems. Rachel Carson has been a sure-footed leader in showing how to widen the context of the problem of "chemical control," for example, and place it in the wider setting of "biological control," simply because nature and man are more than chemistry. The contributors to this volume want to widen the problem of science, technologies and ethical decision to see it as one of "ethical control." Thus the information generated by the sciences and technologies is necessary but not sufficient for an optimal decision on what is best for man. If man is really in God's image—and that is a moral image if it is any image at all—then the biblical view of man is quite pertinent to the problem.

The Institute for Advanced Christian Studies, through specific writing projects and through conferences such as the one that precipitated this volume, seeks to bring some of the more significant issues into sharper focus. The biblical mind needs to be liberated for each generation so that its pertinence and wisdom may be clearly seen and understood. Our era needs desperately to see with fresh sight that Origin and Fount of all that is either mind or matter and is, through his own revelation, the Lord of all meaning. As a kind of "floating" Institute we encourage in-depth scholarship by Christian men and women who want to serve their generation by loving the Lord with their whole minds.

From the many available evangelicals who are specialists in their own disciplines, we have asked several to share their thoughts on the key issues concerning the scientist and ethical decision. These papers were initially contributions to an invitational scholars' conference at the University of Michigan on October 20-21, 1972.

In all these papers is found the tension necessarily felt by fallen man as he tugs at the leash of revealed truth. The presence of a real, if distorted, image of an ethical God in our broken humanity remains the silent testimony that God is finally, in heart and in history, the only sufficient witness to himself.

Besides the actual contributors to this volume, a number of men of science (including medicine and mathematics) served as consultants or advisers. It is a pleasure to recognize their valuable help both at the level of design and articulation: David Lindberg, Orville S. Walters, Kenneth Whitby, Robert D. Knudsen, Donald W. Munro, Gary Collins, Donald DeGraaf, Richard H. Bube, Harold W. Hermann, Jack Swenson, James F. Jekel, Donald C. Boardman, George I. Mavrodes, George J. Jennings, Arthur F. Holmes, David O. Moberg, Martin L. Singewald, and Paul Meehl.

April 1973   *Charles Hatfield*

I
Ethical Principle

Christian Ethics and
Scientific Control
by Henry Stob

W hen one focuses on science and technology, two features of contemporary existence directly traceable to modern man's scientifico-technical behavior come into view and affright. One is the exploitation and pollution of external nature. The other is the chemical, biological and psychological manipulation of man.

The purpose of this essay is to expose this kind of scientific "control" to the scrutiny of Christian ethics.

I shall begin by (1) depicting the rise of Western science and technology; attempt next (2) to set forth a Christian understanding of man's relation to nature; continue (3) by commenting on selected features of the current scientific engagement with man; and end (4) by remarking on the role and use of the Bible in moral decision making.

THE SCIENTIFIC ENTERPRISE

Modern natural science has a character of its own, but it is rooted in the past and has a complex lineage. Christian elements are in it and also motifs inherited from the ancient Hebrews. It has connections with the Hellenic nature studies which culminated in Aristotle, and it reflects the Latin sense of order which was transmitted to the Middle Ages by the Roman Stoics. And, of course, it owes much to the philosophical and methodological impulses generated by the late Renaissance, notably by Francis Bacon and Rene Descartes. In spite of its diverse parentage, however, or perhaps because of it, it has its own unique identity. Its distinctiveness appears when it is compared with the Hebrew, Greek and orthodox-Christian intellectual traditions.

As the Old Testament amply witnesses, the Hebrew attitude toward nature was not analytical and manipulative, but aesthetic and celebrative. Nature was not primarily a problem or puzzle to be solved nor a set of powers and processes to be harnessed, but a sign and symbol of the Creator, calculated to inspire praise and, sometimes, fear. Nature to the pious Israelite was Gothic in its structure. It was a finger pointing away from itself toward heaven and God. Most of it witnessed to God's power and goodness, though parts of it—notably the raging seas—disclosed his wrath and the mystery of the divine abyss. In any case, nature was not a thing apart, an object to be held at a distance and investigated or altered. It was God's creation and it was under his providence. Sheep and cattle could be tended, wild and ferocious beasts could be restrained and the ground could be cultivated—all by the licensing of God—but nature as a whole could only be thankfully and reverently accepted as man's given abode, God's footstool and the arena of his wondrous works. Science, as we have have come to know it, could obviously not develop within a world view of this sort, and all men accordingly agree that, though the Hebrews were notable for religion, they produced and could produce no science.

Science, as almost everything else, took its rise, or else came first to self-consciousness, in Greece. It arose, according to Aristotle, out of curiosity. The Greek wanted to *know*, that is, cognitively to grasp and appropriate the structure, the anatomy, the essence of things. The desire to know these essences might direct a platonizing mind to the contemplation of the pure celestial Exemplars of them or direct an Aristotle to a scrutiny of their embodiment in corporeal existents, but, in either case, the interest was in essences, and the satisfaction of the interest was in understanding. There was no end beyond this. Knowledge was not for power or for any other sort of utility. Knowledge was only to satisfy curiosity; knowledge was for knowledge's sake.

Technology, accordingly, did not develop in Greece. Nature was there to be read and understood, not to be manipulated. More than that, nature—in the sense of mutable phenomena in process—was less the proper object of knowledge than the medium in and through which the proper object of knowledge, the eternal, immutable essences or forms, could be apprehended. Knowledge in Greek thought, whether Platonic or Aristotelian, meant "union with the unchangeable," with the "really real." For this reason, science, as we have come to know it, did not flourish in Greece, even though under Aristotelian auspices the Hellenistic world produced a Ptolemy, Galen, Euclid and Archimedes. There were other reasons, including a disdain of "hands," why Greece did not produce science, but an account of these must wait until we consider the Christian attitude to nature.

Christianity, which is centrally oriented to Christ Jesus, did not, in spite of Marcion, disdain the Old Testament or the Hebrew mind. Nor did it, in spite of Tatian and Tertullian, disdain the Greeks. Christianity is the result of God's gracious act in Jesus Christ and not the natural product of Israel and Hellas. Yet Justin Martyr and Clement of Alexandria were not wholly wrong: Christianity has made these two streams its tributaries. This has several implications which are not presently germane. What is of interest now is that in its distinctive view of nature and science Christianity included elements from both traditions.

By combining the Old Testament concept of *creation* and the Johannine-Greek idea of the *Logos*, Christian thinkers came to recognize and assert that nature is shot through with rationality, and that because of its intelligibility it not only can but should be "known." Lacking a radical doctrine of creation, the Greeks never attained this insight. Besides the immanent Logos there existed for them an independent and essentially intractable "matter" which could not be completely "formed" or rationalized. A corporeal thing or natural process could, therefore, never be rightly "known"—not even by the gods; irrationality and unintelligibility are natural and therefore inexpungable components of all phenomena. This is another reason why a natural science, as distinct from a philosophy of essences, was never developed among the Greeks, but could, and did, flourish on Christian soil.

The biblical doctrine of creation served also to drive out of nature the ancient sky, mountain and fertility gods which, in the heathen view, constituted or inhabited it. It rendered nature secular and thus made it available for inquiry. Because of the absence of the creation doctrine among the Greeks, science could even there not really get off the ground. In the Greek view, nature was not something that had been made *ex nihilo*. It was an eternal, self-generating organism involved in ceaseless circular growth. It was the living, throbbing, but impersonal reproductive matrix from which all things—even the gods—arose and into which they were periodically resolved. The Bible, on the contrary, de-divinizes and de-sacralizes nature. This does not mean that it deprives nature of its life cycles, its vital processes and its web of dynamic relationships with all God's creatures, including man. The Bible does not reduce nature to a machine. But it does declare that nature is creaturely and nondivine, and it thereby licenses science.

From the Bible, too, came the insight that nature is the "ward" of man. This is not a Greek idea. For the Greek, man was a part of nature, wholly caught up in it and obliged to conform to it; he was to live "according to nature." In Christian thought, however, man is conceived as in some sense transcending nature and as obliged to care for it. The notion of transcendence involves "dominion" and the notion of care involves "control." As everyone knows, these concepts lend themselves quite easily to perversion. They can be made to authorize a despotic and exploitive rape of nature. In classical Christian thought, however, "dominion" was hedged about with moral restraints and regulated by religious "praise" (Ps. 8:9). It was recognized that man was put in charge of nature, not as an ultimate master but as a God-appointed servant, steward and husbandman, charged with a development and healing ministry. Consequently the "control" which is allowed and even enjoined must be exercised by man in "godly fear," and, in strict obedience to the law of love, man must direct his dominion toward the true well-being of all God's creatures.

Hebrew, Greek and Christian impulses did not of themselves suffice to produce the science and technology that emerged in the seventeenth century and came in the following centuries to dominate Western culture. Needed was an additional impulse. As it turned out, this impulse was provided by philosophy, more particularly by the philosophy of Descartes.

Descartes professed Christianity and remained until his death a member of the Roman church. But his philosophical conceptions, which gave expression to the anthropocentric humanism of the Renaissance, not only moved science away from the Hebrew "celebrative" and the Greek "contemplative" stances, it also moved it away from the Christian stance of an "understanding, preserving, developing and healing ministry" performed in obedience to God and in accordance with his law of love.

What happened was this: Descartes posited two substances, the *res cogitans* and the *res extensa,* the thinking man and the space-time world outside of him. He not only distinguished these two things, he separated them; and, what is more, he placed them over against each other, meanwhile according to man not merely an ascendancy over nature but a power of determination over it. To justify and accelerate man's ascendancy he diminished nature by regarding all of its components, including living things, as automata—mere "things" as manipulable as stones. To implement man's ascendancy he devised a new logic which divorced subjective reason from transcendental and transcendent attachments (cf. Plato and Augustine), and brought into being a means-end calculus which, concentrating on means, either forgot about ends or adopted them from sub-

or extra-rational sources, like, for example, the "desires" of a comfort-loving public.

In this way "technical reason" came to replace "ontological reason," and men came to be locked in the means-end structure of phenomenological reality, without transcendence, and thus without extra-phenomenological canons of value. By the same token the Creator God, in relation to whom the created universe has its unity and wholeness, was replaced by the "thinking" man who unified the world by subjecting it to a logical calculus employed to make nature serve exclusively "human" ends, where "human" meant "divorced from both God and nature." Lost in all this was man's own immanence in nature and his mediatorship functions within it. Nature, having been reduced to a mere "object," an abstract cognitive *Gegenstand,* a mere pole in the logical subject-object nexus, could be manipulated at will.

This view of things did not of itself produce technology, but it provided a philosophical justification for its unlimited use when and if it should come. Technology came when increased population, growing urbanization and expanding economic wants drove men to tap what seemed to them to be the limitless resources of nature. Descartes' view of nature and knowledge was itself an impetus to produce tools for "control," and the inclination to do so was abetted by Francis Bacon's contention that "knowledge is for power." But deep down it was the human desire first for the satisfaction of basic needs and then for creature comforts that triggered the technological explosion. In response to growing popular demands, partly spontaneous and partly induced by announced possibilities and tempting promises, engineers and other artisans brought nature into the service of man and began to supply the mechanical conveniences with which our present world is filled. So began the industrial revolution.

Based on a Cartesian view of nature and supported by a utopian idea of progress, technology went from strength to strength, creating new wants in the very process of satisfying old ones. Meanwhile most men were unmindful of the fact that nature's resources are finite and fast dwindling, and that industrial wastes were polluting the very air, water and land on which human existence depends. But now we have come to realize that we are in an ecological crisis, and we are puzzled to know how the doom that threatens us can be averted.

It will be my concern in the next section of this paper to consider the theologico-ethical understandings which might provide us with a perspective on the observed developments and with standards for evaluating them. I proceed, then, to consider the man-nature relation: the ecological problem.

THE MAN-NATURE COMPLEX: ECOLOGICAL PROBLEM

There are many ways of organizing Christian truth, but the organization adopted in any instance must be focused on the issue at hand. I am not sure that my organization is maximally adapted to set forth the man-nature problem, but I have, for good or ill, undertaken to arrange the discussion under the heads of Creation, Fall, Redemption.

Creation. The aspect of the problem that is suggested by the concept of creation is the cosmological one of status and position. The question here is: Is man immersed in nature, or does he stand outside it? The question is very old, but it is being asked with new urgency today. In ecological discussions it is dividing men into "inclusivist" and "exclusivist" camps. In a book entitled *Crisis in Eden* (Nashville: Abingdon, 1970), Frederick Elder (a self-styled inclusivist) classified Herbert Richardson and Harvey Cox as exclusivists. They are represented as advocating the divorce of man from nature and as favoring the creation of an artificial in place of the natural environment (city vs. wilderness). Elder represents himself and his associates (notably Loren Eiseley) as wanting to think of man as "an inextricable part of nature" and as called to be in harmony with it, rather than to exercise dominion over it. Seen in historical perspective the issue here raised is one that has always figured in the monist-dualist quarrel.

In the context of the present discussion, a dualist is one who lifts man above and beyond the matrix of nature and thus authorizes him either to flee from it into ideal realms or else to turn upon and assault it. We have already met such a dualist in Descartes. In this particular he betrays a certain kinship with the ancient gnostic and docetic sects which, unlike Descartes, disqualified nature (the corporeal universe) as in some sense evil. Some members of these sects avenged themselves on nature by abusing the body and fouling the fields, thus anticipating the twentieth century. Others, by mystic contemplations and ascetic practices, elevated themselves above the gross reality of nature. If these latter could not be charged with doing positive injury to nature, they could nevertheless be charged with indifference and neglect.

The present growing resentment against a dualistic understanding of the man-nature complex can, therefore, be appreciated. The demand now is for monism. Demanded is that man and nature be brought back together and contemplated as interdependent and complementary parts of one all-embracing Whole. The call is for oneness, harmony, unity and equality. If the call for holism debases man, disclaims his assumed centrality and shatters his pretentions, this, we are assured, is unavoidable and salutary. The present crisis requires that man's kinship with all creatures, and his inclusion in a comprehensive ecological system, be emphatically affirmed.

The monism that underlies these representations calls attention to a truth that no one may ignore, but the monism itself is no more acceptable than the dualism it wishes to replace. Monism always comes at the price of reductionism. Some inclusivists, accordingly, reduce man to the status of nature's lowest common denominator, thus substituting a materialistic or dynamic naturalism for the humanistic idealism they have rejected. Others hominize the whole of nature and thus resuscitate the hylozoism and animism of the primitives, or they develop a pantheistic romanticism marked, among other things, by a pious devotion to daffodils and water fowl.

Christianity knows nothing of a dualism, unless the ontological gap which separates the Creator from the creature be so called. Nor does it recognize a monism, unless it be the unity of all things in the Creator and Redeemer. In any case, it has broken with all intra-cosmic dualisms and monisms. Within the cosmos it recognizes individuality and diversity on the one hand, and interrelatedness and interdependence on the other, but neither separation nor identity anywhere. This applies with special force to man, who is unique in God's creation.

On the one hand, man is dust and thus bound in with nature and with all that nature does and contains. From this point of view all of God's space-time creatures are his kin, he and they are embraced inextricably in a common whole, and with them his fortunes are wrapped up. On the other hand, man is a person who by God's special endowment is able (and enjoined) to relate not only to all creatures horizontally but also to God vertically, and so become the mediator between the two. Herein he resembles the Savior Jesus Christ, in whose image he was made. It follows, I think, that if some formula is required to express man's relation to nature it must be framed in analogy to that of Chalcedon: child of nature and child of God. Here immanence is attended by vicegerency. Here that is given which while not disrupting the ecological nexus, maintains the priority and the unique responsibility of man.

Fall. The question has more than once been raised as to whether through the Fall of man the structures of the cosmos were bent or broken, whether its processes were slowed down or increased, or whether other basic changes took place in nature. I dare go no farther here than to express the opinion that the cosmical structures and processes have throughout time remained essentially the same. It seems clear, however, that nature is caught up in disruptions and that man and nature are involved in conflicts which go beyond the polarities and tensions indigenous to the created world and which, therefore, testify to the presence of sin.

Fortunately, not *all* is conflict; there is unity and coherence,

too. What actually appears is *ambiguity*. This ambiguity arises
from the fact that, though sin is in its very nature alienating and
disruptive, it can operate only within and through the stable
structures of creation. Evil requires the good in order to be at
all, and conflict requires order. This order is maintained by
Providence, not indeed apart from Christ in whom the continued existence of the world has its ground and warrant, yet
"prior" to the ultimate redemption of the whole creation. It is
on account of Providence that, in the realm of what Bonhoeffer
calls the "penultimate," even those who are not (or not yet) in
Christ and are not impelled by Christian motives and purposes
are yet (by the "common" grace of restraint and enlightenment) so under God's direction that hostilities are tempered,
and that some degree of order and cooperation is maintained
throughout the whole of nature.

If, accordingly, one asks whether nature is malignant or
benign, the answer must be that it is both. Its benignity relative
to itself and towards mankind is disclosed in its capacity for,
and nizus towards, self-renewal and self-replenishment. This feature of nature provides ground for hope and optimism in the
present environmental crisis. We can know that, if we stop our
aggrandizements, nature will largely of itself regain the health
which we have destroyed or undermined. But nature is also
"malignant" in that, when untended by a superior intelligence
and will, it can and does create the deserts, jungles and various
noxious things which threaten or discomfit men, that is, those
creatures who, being of a higher order than the surrounding
nature, are required to build cultures and civilizations.

That man in the state of sin has assaulted, plundered and
polluted nature is plain for all to see. But there has, in the past
and present, been "reverence" for it too. And now, whether out
of respect for nature's own individuality and identity or out of
concern for their own survival, men are disposed to end the war
and heal the wounds of nature. Thus good and bad are—also in
the human stance, and even apart from saving grace—commin-
gled. These ambiguities and ambivalences have caused some men

to take up a position in the middle distance. They have proposed that we declare a truce with nature and strike a balance between the rival claims of nature and human culture. They have proposed that we establish a garden-village between the city and the wilderness, and thus let man and nature live in peace and in territorial integrity. On the level of the penultimate there is doubtless merit in this proposal, but it falls far short of the redemptive plan and purpose that was proclaimed and initiated by Jesus Christ.

Redemption. The Christian's relation to nature is, on the creational level, the same as that of any man: He is nature's child and he is its finite lord. On the level of the Fall (which preserves the creational level) the Christian, like every man, is caught up in the ambiguities of existence and must make prudential decisions in the light of the situation and with regard to the available options. But to be a Christian means not only to be a man and involved in sin; it means to be *in Christ* and to be a willing and active participant in his ongoing work of cosmic redemption. This means that the Christian in his relations with nature is controlled by a purpose which in principle lifts him above the levels of tactics and ad hoc decisions and puts him in possession of an all-encompassing strategy: the Christian strategy of involvement, judgment and renewal. These elements in the strategy do, of course, but recapitulate the redemptive events enacted in the world by God in Christ: the Incarnation, Crucifixion and Resurrection. The Christian is called to "repeat" in his own life and person these "acts of God."

In the Incarnation God entered into created reality and, without losing his identity as God, became in a mysterious way "at one" with it. The Christian must do the same with respect to nature. He must veritably and passionately "identify" with it, recognize it as his "own flesh," "accept" it in all of its disruptions and perversions and make no attempt either to escape or nullify it. However, he must not, in his involvement and commitment, forget that in his being he is a product not of nature but of God, that he participates in the "Logos," and that a redemptive role has been assigned to him that, of all God's creatures, only he can play. One thing, and that the most germane, must still be added. Since, in respect to his being, the Christian is "incarnate" by nature and not by love and choice (as is the Lord), he must now, in still stricter imitation of Christ, become "redemptively incarnate." He must, as Christian, deliberatively renounce his technological power and glory and self-sacrificially espouse the cause of nature, not in order to give nature an unwarranted ascendancy but to prepare both it and the race of men for the coming of the Kingdom.

In the Crucifixion of Christ God both passed a *judgment* on the world and opened up a channel for his *grace*. The judgment that he passed was primarily upon the forces of sin and death which had "invaded" his domain, and it was secondarily upon the whole structure of reality which these forces had perverted and despoiled. In the judgment laid upon sin, the divine No! assured sin's final banishment. In the judgment upon man and his environment there was a promise that a "new creation" would replace the old. The Christian must do the same with respect to nature. No "invader" bent upon destruction and perversion should be tolerated; every excessive depletion and every pollution should be avenged. But nature itself must be laid under judgment, not for annihilation but for redemption. Redemption here entails the restructuring and redirection of nature in order that it may be made fit for the effective proclamation of the gospel to all who inhabit it and in order that, under Christ's direction, it may be "prepared" for the final consummation.

In the Resurrection of Christ the future of the world is guaranteed. The resurrection assures us that, no matter what nature does and no matter what men do, God's good purposes will prevail. This truth should, of course, tempt no Christian into complacency, but only enlist him for cooperation in the realization of a goal that, by the determination of God, will certainly be reached. Nothing can *compel* and nothing can *hinder* God's grace; his good purposes *will* prevail. But Christians may know that their engagements with nature and the ecological problem are taken by Christ himself as faith in him and his purposes, and as contributing to the realization of the new paradise he has projected.

It should also be observed that, if we are in Christ, we are constituted, as he is, priests, prophets and kings. It has always been the function of a priest to *conserve* the things that God has given, and we may thus conclude that, in respect to nature, we have been charged with a custodial responsibility. Because conservation can atrophy into conservatism, Christ has also made us prophets who *criticize* the status quo and urge men on to better things. And because what God has given and allowed us to develop must be put into the service of the Kingdom, he has appointed us kings or *administrators*, who, in their ministrations, are concerned for nothing so much as the moral and spiritual development of man, the whole man in his ecological context.

Here it should be observed that it is not nature as such, or in isolation, that God is concerned to preserve or develop. What he intended when he created the world, what he purposed when, in his Son he died for it, and what in Christ's Resurrection is guaranteed, is a community, a fellowship of persons, a "kingdom" or "city" set down in a redeemed and renewed environment, a new heaven and a new earth. None of us, nor all of us together, can bring that city and its pacific and indispensable environment into being. Only God in Christ can do that. But we are enjoined to work, both upon men and nature, with the Kingdom in view, that so we may "prepare the way of the Lord."

THE MAN-MAN COMPLEX: THE BIO-MEDICAL PROBLEM
Arising out of science and technology is another matter that is bothering sensitive Christians. It concerns man's scientific relation to and "control" or "manipulation" of man, and it yields what has become known as the bio-medical problem. Science, armed with technical reason and accustomed to treat a cognitive

Gegenstand as a mere object, has asked the "how" question as this relates to human processes such as cerebration, reproduction and social response, and has not only employed manipulative techniques upon man but is making him the object of scientific experimentation.

What I have to say about this lacks the thoroughness and precision that the subject deserves, but perhaps enough will be said to bring the matter into the open.

Because man is a social being with intelligence and will, he not only *is* related to other men, he *has related* himself to them in various ways, out of various motives and to various ends. His having done so is a token of and a witness to his humanity, "address" and "addressability" being integral features of humanness.

What concerns us at present, however, is that specific type of relating which is known as "scientific" and which takes the form of "control." Whether this type of relating is really an "address" in the best and deepest sense of that term is a question we shall have to bear in mind. At this juncture I shall let it lie and do no more than remark that it is very old. Besides the unstructured and spontaneous person-to-person encounters of human beings and besides the social encounters mediated through groups and institutions, there have always been "control-encounters" as well, and these have from earliest times been regulated and directed by sciences developed for the purpose of such control. So, for the control of groups, jurisprudence and military science were developed. On the side of mind, the sciences of philosophy, ethics, rhetoric, aesthetics and the like were developed to shape and direct the three faculties of the soul—intellect, will and emotion. And, of course, on the side of body there developed the sciences of pharmacology, physiology and anatomy, from which flowed the art of medicine. In the construction of these sciences and in the perfecting of control techniques, moral issues sometimes surfaced, as, for example, when inoculation was proposed or when cadavers were utilized for anatomical studies. But, on the whole, scientific control on the one hand and ethics on the other have quite peacefully co-existed.

With the rapid increase of bio-medical knowledge in the last decades, however, and with the amazing refinement of tools and techniques of physical and psychological control, the ethical issue is again rising to the surface—so markedly, indeed, that physicians who stand midway between the theoretical scientist and the lay populace, and who must "perform" at that level, are asking anxiously for moral guidance.

What, then, are the specific questions being asked? What are the problems which need solving? What are the practices, actual or proposed, which require Christian analysis and assessment? At a Colloquium on Ethical Dilemmas from Medical Advances held under the auspices of the American College of Physicians at San Francisco in 1967, the members of the Colloquium considered the moral issues that arise in the following areas:

(1) scientific experimentation on human subjects,

(2) the choice of who is to live and who is not to live (contraception, abortion and infanticide of monsters),

(3) the artificial prolongation of life (by such means as dialysis and transplantation of organs),

(4) the patient's right to die with dignity (prolonged resuscitation, euthanasia),

(5) the psychochemical manipulation of human intelligence,

(6) the genetic effect of medical advances and possible planned manipulation of the genetic basis of the human race, and

(7) the effects on human beings of overpopulation, environmental pollution and testing of nuclear weapons.

This is a very formidable list of issues (even if it does not include *in vitro* conception, androids and other things), and I must here declare, even though it is presumptuous and indelicate to do so, that I shall, as much for want of competence as for want of space, address myself neither to all of them nor to any of them. What I do propose to do is to comment on what I think are some typical features of the current scientific engagement with man. My remarks on these features will, at the same time, disclose what I think must be respected and/or kept inviolate in man's nature and being by any science wishing to exercise control over it.

1. One feature of science, and not merely the science of man, is its apparent inability to arrest its own momentum and to stop short of putting into practice the knowledge and skills it has acquired. This is another way of saying, I suppose, that knowledge, for most members of the scientific community, is never merely for contemplation but also always for utility. This *does* make *prima facie* sense, but it also raises a moral problem. Is it true, as Karl Rahner has said, that "there is really nothing possible for man that he ought not to do"? I suggest that it is not true. "Can" does not imply "may." Between the ability to do something and the moral permission to do it lies a whole area of ethical reflection, an area which science too often overleaps, or over which it is insensitively carried by its own momentum. Unfortunately, this attitude is generally carried over into the larger community. A woman is told, "Abortions can be safely done." She replies, "I very much would like it done." In many instances it then *gets* done; the moral issue is screened out.

2. In the sciences engaged with man, man is, when made an experimental subject, sometimes animalized; and this means, once more, that the religious and moral dimensions of his being are ignored and also that he is unclothed. A case in point is provided by the studies in the physiology and psychology of sexual intercourse undertaken by Drs. Masters and Johnson. Their subjects were sometimes unmarried and, in at least one instance, total strangers to each other. But since this was a scientific experiment, this circumstance was considered either irrelevant or calculated to enlarge the scope of the investigation and increase the value of the findings. What offends in all this is that the inquiry was made on the assumption that there is no moral law of chastity and that there is no privacy. But, of course, the assumption cannot be granted. God does forbid for-

nication and adultery. And he also wishes to reserve a place for privacy. And the preeminent place he has reserved for it is in sexual union. In this sacramental union of love and commitment, which symbolizes Christ's oneness with his Church, no witnesses may intrude. In the experiments of the doctors the canons of morality and the canons of reserve were violated, and in the process man was brutalized.

3. In the sciences engaged with man, man is sometimes *robotized.* In Anthony Burgess' novel, *A Clockwork Orange,* this is dramatically portrayed. In the story the antisocial behavior of Alex is removed by "conditioning" procedures administered by the state. We are dealing here, it is true, with a story only, but the story was written to alert the public to the fact that science does now have the resources to "by-pass" the will and reduce a man to something like a puppet. The fact that this sort of manipulation is within the power of science does not justify the employment of such power or demonstrate that man is actually something else than a responsible person with free will. If it demonstrates anything, it demonstrates that demonic forces are still loose in the world and can bring man into temporary captivity. Science, however, should not ally itself with the demons.

4. A reigning idea in the sciences engaged with man is that of *psychosomatic unity.* One need not immediately quarrel with that idea. It goes back at least as far as Aristotle and was transmitted to the modern world by Thomas Aquinas. One is entitled to prefer it to what is called the "ghost in the machine" theory of Plato. Yet Christians who embrace the psychosomatic theory should realize that they can do so only if they find a ground for *psyche* and a ground for *soma* above these two, in God. Otherwise, one is bound to fall either into idealism or into materialism. With Plato and Kant currently in disrepute, I suspect that most non-Christian scientists fall into materialism and locate the foundations of life, intelligence and spiritual aspiration in matter. This misleads many scientists into thinking that man can be structured, renewed and advanced by biochemical means. This is as mistaken as the idealist thesis that matter is

mere appearance and that the body is a function of the soul.
The fact is that mind and body are equally real and legitimate
aspects of the cosmos. They are related to each other in various
ways, but the relation that holds between them is not one of
unilateral domination but one of mutual dependence. Both are
created and neither is absolute. Each is correlative to the other.
It is only by recognizing this and not by exalting one at the
expense of the other that the true unity of the cosmos, and of
man, is seen. That unity lies not in the lordship of one cosmic
aspect over another, but in the Lordship of God over all and in
that divinely ordained structure in which each finds its peculiar
place and function.

5. A conviction governing a great deal of the scientific concern with man is that man is not a finished product of creation
but is an unfinished, malleable and open-ended something,
which, having been produced by mother nature, is being moved
by evolutionary forces into a promising future. It is this conviction which justifies for many scientists the various forms of
genetic engineering. Bio-medical science, in this context, is not
concerned, as it was in the past, simply to support or heal; it is
concerned to program and direct, and in this way to be as
"creative" as nature itself. A Christian should, I think, not ignore the dynamic aspects of human existence, but neither
should he lose sight of the static structures which set "limits" to
man's nature and within which the elements of potentiality are
confined. Because man is divinely structured I find it hazardous,
if not impious, to tamper with the genetic pool. To tamper with
the genes seems to me to "outrun" God into an unknown future and to exercise an "elective" discrimination mere men do
not possess.

6. Despite the fact that bio-medical science is still captive to
the spirit of specialization and is still attached to the abstract
method which tends to ignore the religious and moral dimensions of man, there seems nevertheless to be a growing awareness in parts of the scientific community of the need for inter-
disciplinary studies. Insofar as this awareness exists it may rep-

resent a breakthrough in the consciousness of investigators that man is indeed a Whole, that he runs the gamut of the created universe, that he is a microcosm, and that by the nonsynthetic, noncomprehensive procedures of classical natural science he can be neither understood nor preserved as human.

THE BIBLE AND MORAL DECISION MAKING

I have in the foregoing not only tried to lay a Christian basis for a moral assessment of contemporary scientifico-technical behavior, but have also, at several junctures, hazarded such assessments. I shall not summarize these now because, being what they are, they can do without reiteration. What I propose to do instead is make a concluding remark about the role and use of the Bible in moral decision making.

The Bible is for Christians the ultimate moral guide: It is our rule for conduct as it is for faith. But how does the Bible function as a guide? And how do we distill from it directions for our lives and warrant for our decisions?

The thing primarily to be observed is that specific, minutely detailed obligations are seldom laid upon the conscience in the revelation God has given. If we exscind, as we must, the carefully formulated civil statues and ceremonial regulations which helped to define the path of duty for the Old Testament saint, there is very little left in the Bible of specific injunction concerning the concrete problems of everyday life. If a man wants to know whether he may attend an X-rated movie or conduct scientific experiments on human subjects, whether he may drink whiskey or make use of contraceptives, whether he may join the AFL or test nuclear weapons, whether he may swim on Sunday or approve of euthanasia, whether he may dance or conduct experiments in cloning, whether he may follow a career on the stage or license the transplantation of human organs, whether he may play cards or engage in the psychochemical manipulation of human intelligence, he will look in vain for a ready-made answer in any one of the sixty-six books of the Bible. The Bible is not a law book. The reasons for this are not hard to discover. There are, I should think, at least three of them.

In the first place, when prophets, evangelists or apostles speak in the Bible on moral issues, they always do so in the light of two magnitudes—the gospel on the one hand and the situation on the other. Permanent in this constellation is the gospel; evanescent is the situation. When, therefore, they make specific moral judgments—as, for example, St. Paul does about women speaking in the church or keeping their heads covered—it is necessary to disentangle the gospel principle from the time- and culture-conditioned application of it which he then made under the guidance of the Spirit. The concrete prescription made is binding on no Christian—the change of situation annuls or compromises it. The gospel principle remains our guide, but, being general, it needs recurrent interpretation and application, for history moves on and situations change. The first reason, therefore, why the Christian cannot live by rule is this: The proper understanding of the Bible precludes it.

In the second place, no specific rule, embodying a single univocal meaning, could ever be formulated and made to apply in the same way to all people at all times in all places. From the nature of the case a rule is static, fixed, abstract, whereas life, to which the rule is meant to apply, is dynamic, variable and concrete. No strict correlation can, therefore, be made between the two. A rule has no capacity, and a man who lives by rules has no opportunity, to estimate and respond to such important moral variables as motive, degree of temptation, age, alternative courses of action, conflict of duties and the like. A tight prescription can never be saddled upon a vital process. This is why legalists who like to hedge in the principles of morals with ordinances find themselves compelled, in order to keep pace with life's complexities, to heap rule upon rule. They must frame a rule to define a previous rule, a rule for breaking rules, a rule for adjusting conflicting rules, a rule for keeping rules, and so on *ad infinitum,* in a frantic attempt to fix and contain what no mere rule or set of rules can possibly contain. And this is the second reason, I presume, why the Scriptures do not press God's claim upon us in the form of a multitude of detailed ordinances.

The third reason seems to me to lie in the fact that living by rules is not calculated to call into play those faculties of will and judgment which it is the purpose of the Lord to develop in us. It is evidently God's will not only that we should *do* right but also that we should *be* right. He is concerned not only that our external deeds should hit the mark but also that our characters should come out strong and well-rounded. But character, strength of will, keenness of moral perception and the habit of fervent prayer cannot be formed in one by requiring him to do no more than manipulate a legalistic calculus. Saints are made when men, aided by God's Spirit, guided by the eternal principles of his Word and stirred by the example of those who have gone before, of whom Christ is chief, are thrown out into the complex world and forced in the exercise of their God-given liberty to *discover* God's will in study, prayer and effort, so that at last, after falling often and being forgiven often, they grow into maturity and attain something of the fullness of the stature of Christ.

If it is not obedience to rules, regulations and ordinances, what is it, then, that the Scriptures enjoin? The answer is that it is *love* they enjoin—perfect love, Christian love, supernatural love, the love displayed by God in Christ upon the tree, the love which only Christ imparts—the love that suffereth long and is kind, that envieth not, that vaunteth not itself and is not puffed up, that doth not behave itself unseemly, that seeketh not its own, is not provoked, taketh not account of evil, that rejoiceth not in unrighteousness, but rejoiceth with the truth, the love that beareth all things, believeth all things, hopeth all things, endureth all things. This is enjoined upon the conscience. This is God's will for us.

If it be asked, What does love mean? the answer is that the very least it means is set down in the Ten Commandments. Although these commandments, like love, are general, they do

provide us, together with other Scripture, a set of principles that can lead us through the moral labyrinth. What they say, abstracted from their Israelitish form, is something like this:
He who commands you is the Savior.

1. You are to acknowledge no other God than the Creator, Redeemer and Judge disclosed in Jesus Christ.

2. You are to commit yourselves ultimately to God and not to some secular cause or institution held to be representative of him.

3. Your posture in the presence of God can only be that of reverence and awe, *and* his name is never to be used as a handle with which to manipulate him.

4. You are to observe the rhythm of life and neither separate nor confuse the ultimate and the penultimate.

5. You must love your parents as persons, and you must respect their authority, as well as the authority of all who have been given jurisdiction, as vicegerents of God.

6. You must preserve and enhance life.

7. Unlike animals, you must put sex in a moral and spiritual context.

8. Man's property, as well as his person, is to be kept inviolable for the purposes of love.

9. A man's person is to be respected, and a channel is to be kept open for the actualization of his possibilities.

10. All selfishness is to be resolutely banned.

Besides all this we have the great redemptive events, the basic indicatives on which the Christian imperatives are based.

It is these things which comprise the Christian guide in morals. God help us to discern and follow them!

Love and Duty
by Ronald H. Nash

Professor Stob is to be commended for the job he has done. However, I believe the temporal limits within which he had to work forced him to telescope the important things he wished to say at the end of his paper. The question of how Christian ethics can aid the scientist or indeed any man in determining his moral duty is important enough to warrant an amplification of Stob's remarks. This is especially true, I think, because of some ambiguities in Stob's discussion that require clarification. I wish to base my extension and clarification of Stob's remarks on three distinctions familiar to every student of contemporary ethics.

THE DISTINCTION BETWEEN PRINCIPLES AND RULES

Let us define a moral principle as a *general* moral prescription, general in the sense that it is intended to cover a large number of instances. Moral rules, on the other hand, will be regarded as more *specific* moral prescriptions that are, in fact, applications of principles to more concrete situations. There are corresponding advantages and disadvantages to principles and rules. The advantage of moral principles is that they are less subject to change. Because of the larger number of instances they apply to, they tend to a greater degree of universality. The disadvantage of any moral principle is its vagueness. By virtue of the fact that it covers so many types of situation, it is often difficult to know exactly when it applies. Rules, however, have the advantage of being much more specific. Their problem results from their changeability. Because they are so closely tied to situations, when the situation changes, the rule may have to be changed as well. For example, St. Paul warned the Christian women of Corinth not to worship with their heads uncovered. Some Christians have mistakenly regarded Paul's advice as a moral principle that should be observed by Christian women in every culture at all times. But a study of the conditions of ancient Corinth reveals that the Corinthian prostitutes identified themselves to their prospective customers by keeping their heads uncovered. In the light of this, it seems clear that Paul's advice was not a moral principle intended to apply to Christians of all generations but rather a rule that applied only to the women of Corinth and women in similar situations.

I recognize that the distinction I am drawing here suffers from a degree of impreciseness. This is due in part to the fact that the difference between a principle and rule is sometimes relative. That is, Scripture actually presents a hierarchy of moral prescriptions beginning at the most general level with the duty to love. This duty to love is then further broken down into the duties to love God and love man (Mt. 22:37-40) and then still further into the more specific duties of the Decalogue (Rom. 13:9-10). And, of course, the still more specific duties spelled out in the New Testament such as the prohibition against the lustful look and hatred are further specifications of the Ten Commandments (Mt. 5:21-32). My distinction is a relative one that suggests that wherever you have two scriptural injunctions, one of which is derived from the other and which is more specific, you can regard the more specific as the rule and the other as the principle. It is possible to read 1 Corinthians 13 in this way. First Paul proposes love as a moral duty binding on all men. Then he proceeds to provide specific rules about how a loving agent will behave; e.g., he will be kind, patient, etc.

Now let us apply our distinction between principles and rules to what Stob has said. I have in mind such statements as the following: ". . . There is very little left in the Bible of specific

injunction concerning the concrete problems of everyday life."
Or to take another example, Stob wrote that the man looking
for specific guidance regarding complex moral decisions in this
generation "will look in vain for a ready-made answer in any
one of the sixty-six books of the Bible." I am quite confident
that Stob does not mean to imply what such statements will
suggest to the average reader. There are a great many specific
injunctions in the Bible regarding concrete problems. While
many of these may be specific moral pronouncements that were
tied to specific situations that no longer apply (such as the case
of the Corinthian women), the Bible also contains many moral
prescriptions not restricted by time and place.

Given our distinction, I think we can agree that what Stob
meant to say was the following: (1) The New Testament did
give first-century Christians plenty of rules. But of course, they
were rules that covered situations that contemporary Christians
no longer face, such as Paul's injunction against eating meat
offered to idols. (2) The New Testament does not give *us* (that
is, twentieth-century man) rules regarding our specific situations. The reason for this is obvious. The rules one does find in
the New Testament were first-century rules given to cover first-
century situations. A first-century book that did purport to give
moral rules to twentieth-century man would have been unintelligible to readers in the intervening nineteen hundred years.
What moral help could the Romans or Ephesians have derived
from such moral rules as "Thou shalt not attend X-rated
movies" or "It is wrong to use LSD"? (3) The New Testament
also contains moral principles equally binding on men of all
generations. (4) Even a consideration of first-century rules can
enable us to infer the more general principles behind them,
principles that do apply to us today. While it may be unimpor-
tant today whether Christian women keep their heads covered,
it is important that they avoid provocative dress and behavior.
While few Christians in our generation are bothered by pagan
butchers who have offered their wares as a sacrifice to a false
god, we can all profit from the principle that we should do

nothing that might cause a weaker brother to stumble.

I certainly do not wish to suggest that Scripture presents us with a casuistic system of morality in which specific moral duties can always be deduced from more general moral statements. Casuistry always leads to a type of legalism which is condemned by Scripture. But I do think a recognition of a biblical hierarchy of rules and principles is useful in helping us determine our duty.

RIGHT ACTS AND MORALLY GOOD ACTIONS

By means of this distinction, Sir David Ross, a twentieth-century British philosopher, meant to draw attention to the fact that any moral behavior can be viewed from at least two perspectives: (1) Is the moral behavior fitting, is it the right thing to do? The rightness of an act has nothing to do with the agent's reasons for performing it. An act's rightness is determined solely by whether it was or was not the correct, the fitting, the proper thing to do in that case. To help a little old lady across the street is the right thing to do (providing, of course, that she wishes to cross the street). It is certainly more fitting than to push her in front of a moving automobile. But obviously one can do all sorts of *right acts* for the wrong reasons. And so this led Ross to the second part of his distinction, *morally good actions.* (2) An action is morally good if the agent's motives or intentions were good.

Given the distinction between right acts and morally good actions, four possibilities exist. (a) It is possible to have a right act that is also a morally bad action, that is, the person does the right thing but for the wrong reason. (b) It is possible to have a morally good action that is a wrong act. In this case, the man's intentions were good but he still did the wrong thing. (c) It is possible to have both a wrong act and a bad action. I suppose this kind of behavior would require that the agent be both morally perverse and stupid. (d) And finally, it is possible to have a morally good action that is also the right act.

Stob objected to "living by rules" on the ground that such

conduct fails "to call into play those faculties of will and judgment which it is the purpose of the Lord to develop in us. It is
evidently God's will not only that we should *do* right but also
that we should *be* right. He is concerned not only that our
external deeds should hit the mark but also that our characters
should come out strong and well-rounded." Without doubt,
God is concerned that we both do the right thing and do it for
the proper reasons. But presumably even God recognizes that
before we can do the right thing, we have to know what the
right thing is, that is, we need some knowledge of either a rule
or principle. So I fail to see how Stob's point succeeds in eliminating the need for rules and principles. Furthermore, since a
large segment of the human race will persist in refusing to act
out of love to God and other men, society still is better off
when men perform right acts (obey the rules) even if their
motivation is deficient.

ACT-AGAPISM AND RULE-AGAPISM
This distinction was first suggested, I believe, by Professor William Frankena of the University of Michigan. *Act-agapism* is
another name for the situation ethics of Joseph Fletcher. This is
the view that Christian ethics imposes no duty other than the
duty to love. In determining what he should do, the situationist
declares, the Christian should face the moral situation and ask
himself what the loving thing to do is in this particular situation. There are no rules or principles that prescribe how love
will react. Indeed, each loving individual is free to react in any
way he thinks is consistent with love as he understands it. The
point to act-agapism is, then, that Christian ethics provides absolutely no universal principles or rules. Nothing is intrinsically
good except love; nothing intrinsically bad but non-love. One
can never prescribe in advance what a Christian should do. Love
may, depending on the situation, find it necessary to lie, to
steal, even presumably to fornicate, blaspheme and worship
false gods. The only absolute is love.
I am quite confident that Stob does not intend to recom-

mend a situation ethic to us. Rather, he is proposing a variation of what Frankena calls *rule-agapism*. There are two possible ways of formulating rule-agapism. (1) It may be understood as that position which holds that love is insufficient in itself to provide moral guidance for each and every moral act. Love requires the further specification of principles or rules which suggest the proper ways in which love should be manifested. Rule-agapism in this first sense means a love-ethic that recognizes love's need for guidance from divinely revealed moral truth. (2) Rule-agapism may also be understood in a second way. God has revealed moral principles which are to guide man in his moral decisions. The ultimate justification of each moral principle is love. In other words, the rule-agapist says, it is impossible to determine what we should do in each and every particular situation on the basis of love alone. We need principles and laws which find their ground in love.

THE MORAL DECISION

Let us now see if, given the distinctions we have considered, it is possible to distinguish biblical ethics from both legalism and situation ethics. We shall also attempt to say something about how biblical ethics can provide guidance in moral situations.

Situation ethics can be pictured in this way:

THE MORAL AGENT
(love)

THE MORAL SITUATION

According to this view, the moral agent has no rules or principles to guide him in making moral decisions. All he has is love, presuming that he has it to begin with and knows what love is. Given the situation, the act-agapist claims, love is sufficient to tell the agent what he should do. This view is defective for at least two reasons: (1) "Love" is ambiguous and (2) man is a sinner and thus is incompetent to judge the demands of love.

Legalistic ethics can be pictured in this way:

THE MORAL LAW

THE MORAL AGENT

Notice the omission of love in our picture of legalism. Whatever the legalist may say about love in theory, what brands him as a legalist is his ignoring of love (and other motives) in practice. As Stob points out, legalism ignores the weightier matters of the law and should be condemned as unbiblical. The legalist also ignores the finer points of the situation, such as the degree of temptation. Legalism does not follow from a concern with moral principles alone. It follows when the agent ignores other factors important in moral decisions.

How then should we picture biblical ethics?

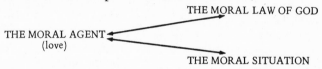

THE MORAL LAW OF GOD

THE MORAL AGENT
(love)

THE MORAL SITUATION

Biblical ethics recognizes three poles to the moral decision: (1) the need for as complete a knowledge of the situation as is possible (contra legalism); (2) the need for as complete a knowledge of God's law as possible (contra situation ethics); (3) the need for the moral agent to act in Christian love. A deficiency with respect to any one of these poles will make a correct moral decision difficult or even impossible. Let us consider some of the things that make many moral decisions difficult.

(1) With respect to his knowledge of the situation, no human being can know enough about any situation to make an infallible moral decision. Suppose a doctor has responsibility for the administration of a kidney machine. He has only one machine but has five critically ill patients who will die without the machine. The doctor must decide which patient will live and which four will die. The doctor cannot possibly know enough about each patient and his family. This type of situation is

especially tragic because there is no decision open to the physician that will not issue in pain and suffering for a number of human beings. Or consider a scientist who is working on a new weapon. Can he possibly foresee all the good and evil that will result from his work? Is he responsible if his research can be used for both good and evil and other men choose to utilize his work for evil ends? To whatever degree, therefore, our knowledge of the situation is limited, so too will our knowledge of our duty be uncertain.

(2) With respect to our knowledge of God's law, other complications can cloud our moral decisions. If a man does not know God's law or cannot determine which principle relates to his particular situation, he will have trouble. No doubt this is one area in which the work of the Holy Spirit is relevant in Christian ethics. That is, while the Holy Spirit does not reveal new moral truth, he does illumine the meaning or application of already revealed truth. Additional problems arise when we are confronted by a conflict of moral principles, that is, cases where every course of action open to us requires that we violate some moral principle.

(3) And finally, which Christian can be completely sure of his motives? We have all known Christians who were always able to rationalize just those courses of action that worked to their own benefit. Which of us can be completely certain that we are not influenced by subconscious motivations that are sub-Christian or anti-Christian?

I am trying to throw some light on why it is sometimes so difficult for Christians to determine their duty. There are times, many times I am afraid, when we just do not know enough about ourselves, the situation or the moral law which applies. I do not wish to suggest that our problem is one of knowledge alone. As we all know too well, weakness of will can also hinder our moral decision making although presumably genuine love would so transform our wills that this problem would disappear or this weakness could be effectively countered.

How does God judge us in the ambiguous situations of life?

Let it be clear that God is not a utilitarian: His ultimate criterion is not the consequences of our acts. Perhaps we should give
thanks for this. God looks upon the heart. We are judged if we
break God's commandments—this much is certain. But in those
cases where we may not know which commandment applies or
where we may have incomplete knowledge of the situation,
God's judgment will take into account not the rightness of the
act (something that we ourselves are unable to determine in
such ambiguous situations) but the goodness of the action.

Let us, to the measure of our knowledge and to the ability
God gives us, do the right thing. But let us even more, since this
is something within our control, do the good thing.

Descartes, Kant and the Development of Science
by Stanley Obitts

P rofessor Stob's paper is a notable addition to the growing list of theologies of nature which have appeared in the last five or six years. They are designed, sometimes only implicitly, to exonerate Christianity from the accusation brought against it by Kenneth Boulding, Lynn White, Jr., and others. That accusation is, as we all know, that the Christian view of nature provided the theoretical and religious justification for the insensitive exploitation and manipulation of the natural world and man in which our scientifico-technological society is engaging.

A PROVOCATIVE ATTACK

The address by Lynn White, Jr., to the American Association for the Advancement of Science in 1966, published in the March 10, 1967, issue of *Science* with the title "The Historical Roots of Our Ecologic Crises" was especially successful in provoking defensive responses from Christian thinkers of all stripes.

White's argument was that because Christianity, particularly in its Western version, is more anthropocentric than any other religion and because it believes God became a man, it views man as sharing in God's transcendence of nature, more than any other religion does. The result, he says, is that "Christianity, in absolute contrast to ancient paganism and Asia's religions (except, perhaps, Zoroastrianism), not only established a dualism of man and nature but also insisted that it is God's will that man exploit nature for his proper ends."[1] To make matters worse, natural theology in the Latin West had become by the early thirteenth century an attempt to understand God's thinking through learning about his creation. The doctrine of creation underlying this thereby came to provide a theological justification of science, and later, technology. In White's words "modern science is an extrapolation of natural theology, and . . . modern technology is at least partly to be explained as an Occidental, voluntarist realization of the Christian dogma of man's transcendence of, and rightful mastery over, nature." "But," he goes on to apply his point, "as we now recognize, somewhat over a century ago science and technology—hitherto quite separate activities—joined to give mankind powers which, to judge by many of the ecologic effects, are out of control. If so, Christianity bears a huge burden of guilt."[2]

Instead of the "orthodox Christian arrogance toward nature," White opts for "a unique sort of pan-psychism of all things animate and inanimate, designed for the glorification of their transcendent Creator," a view which he finds in the teachings of St. Francis of Assisi. St. Francis, we are told, saw clearly the need for the virtue of humility by man, not just as an individual, but also as a species. In place of man's monarchy over creation, St. Francis wished to establish "a democracy of all God's creatures," says White approvingly.[3]

Kenneth Boulding, in his analysis of the problem authorized by the National Council of Churches, goes even further in suggesting a remedy. He advises going to Asian religions to dispel "any illusions about being able to conquer nature."[4]

The well-known Christian philosopher of science, Ian G. Barbour, finds the influence of Greek dualism at the root of the alleged orthodox Christian disdain of nature. By setting the body and soul in strong distinction, the classical theologian lost sight of the Biblical stress upon man as a social being, a person-in-community. The consequence was the acceptance of the Greek view of the body as tainted with evil. But this can be rectified by a recognition of "man's fundamental unity with nature" and the adoption of a "new formulation of the idea of divine immanence" patterned after the "process theology" of Alfred North Whitehead, declares Barbour.[5]

But our purpose is not to attempt a survey of the ever expanding number of significantly different entries into this new game of making orthodox Christianity the whipping boy for today's scientifico-technological crisis. Nor will the varying revisions of a Christian theology of nature be searched for their common elements, although in passing it may be pointed out that the tendency they all seem to share in moving toward some form of pan-psychism, pantheism or a process metaphysic bodes ill for the radical neo-orthodox rejection of divine immanence.

DESCARTES' METAPHYSICAL DUALISM

Professor Stob has claimed to find in Descartes' metaphysical dualism the sufficient condition by way of a philosophical justification for the present subservience of science to a technology which keeps science from celebrating the Creator with the Hebrews, contemplating the essences of reality with the Greeks, and controlling God's intelligible creation in godly fear and in obedience to the law of love with the classical Christians. Being a rationalist, Descartes allowed his postulation of two kinds of substances to work to the disadvantage of matter-substance and to the advantage of mind-substance.

Furthermore, we are told, Descartes went along with Renaissance anthropocentric humanism by placing the clearly and distinctly thinking human mind in charge of the now separate material world, thereby displacing God. Also eliminated was the notion of transcendent nature held by the Greek-thinking Christian theologians from Augustine down through the medieval period. The resulting loss of "man's own immanence in nature and his mediatorship functions within it" permitted Francis Bacon's new inductive scientific method to be employed for the gaining of knowledge which gave power for the purpose of satisfying man's creaturely needs, with little regard for the object being controlled, be it the material world or one's fellow man.

Having traced back to Descartes in this fashion the philosophical cause of today's scientifico-technical exploitation of
nature and manipulation of man, Stob jumps to what he calls
his theologico-ethical understandings of the man-nature and
man-man relations.

However, it is my contention that the present state of subservience of science to technology is not adequately understood
until the role Kant has played is grasped. The radical separation
of man from God and nature, which characterizes the present
mood, could not have been possible without Kant. Therefore, it
is the Kantian attempt to put value back into the world of facts,
and the theological responses to this attempt, rather than the
Cartesian exclusion of value from the world of facts with which
Stob could profitably have spent some time.

It is, of course, beyond question that Descartes' division of
reality into two metaphysically different kinds, mental and material, promoted a mechanistic view of the world studied by
science, the hypothesis of God being no longer needed by the
scientists. It is also true that Descartes' substantival dualism set
the stage for the philosophic drift into the skepticism of British
empiricism culminating in Hume, or else the construction of
unverifiable metaphysical systems by the Continental ration-
alists. But while we who come after Kant know the use he made
of these two philosophic streams coming out of Descartes'
dualism, the age of the Enlightenment, which stood between
Descartes and Kant, did not.

When the scientist Laplace opts for a mechanism in which
there is no use for the hypothesis of God, he does so because he
subscribes to the Enlightenment's conviction in the rationality
and orderliness of the world being disclosed by science. Other
scientists, Newton being the outstanding example, do find the
hypothesis of God useful, at least for philosophical purposes.
But whether they dabble in the philosophy of science or not,
and whether they articulate a theology of nature or not, the
scientists of the Enlightenment believed in a rationally ordered
real world as the object of their investigations. If they had

perceived the implications of Hume's empiricism, their conception of what they were doing and why would have been shattered. But it was not until the young philosophy professor Kant, the paragon of the Enlightenment man, read Hume and was rudely awakened from his dogmatic slumbers, as he puts it, that the beginning of the end of man's confidence in his ability to understand his world and his optimistic espousal of a moral theory based on self-respect, decency and the dignity of his fellow men came about.

Just one quotation will suffice to indicate the lack of comprehension for a full century after Descartes of the incipient skepticism in Descartes which Hume was the first to draw out in the middle of the eighteenth century. Montesquieu begins his great work on social anthropology, entitled *The Spirit of the Laws* (1748), with these sentiments: "Laws in their most general signification are the necessary relations arising from the nature of things. In this sense all beings have their laws: the Deity His laws, the material world its laws, the intelligences superior to man their laws, the beasts their laws, man his laws."[6]

This mood, typical of the Enlightenment, indicates the great extent to which the metaphysics of the medieval era, with its confidence in the rationality, orderliness and lawfulness of the world under God had survived in the minds of most of the educated public down through the eighteenth century. It is hardly the mood taken by the scientifico-technological society decried by Lynn White, Jr., Stob and others. Hence the dualism between those wishing to immerse man in nature and those wishing to keep man apart from nature, the "inclusivists" and "exclusivists" of Frederick Elder's *Crisis in Eden,* is not so clearly linked with Descartes' metaphysical dualism as Stob seems to think. Neither the monistic union of man with nature nor the dualistic setting of man over against nature in an exploitative stance, of which we read so much today, appeared during the century or more of the dominance of Cartesian metaphysics, that is, from the death of Descartes in 1650 until the appearance of Kant's epoch-making *Critique of Pure Reason* in 1781.

Indeed, the approach toward the world of scientific concern, for which we cited Montesquieu as a mid-eighteenth century spokesman, had not changed much at all from the orientation Descartes himself gave it as described in his autobiographical *Discourse on Method* (1637). There he points out that out of its own resources metaphysics should be able to provide a general scheme of nature. Here is how he puts it:

I have first tried to discover generally the principles or first causes of everything that is or can be in the world . . . [deriving them from] certain germs of truth which are naturally existent in our souls. After that I considered which were the primary and most ordinary effects which might be deduced from these causes, and it seems to me that in this way I discovered the heavens, the stars, and earth, and even on the earth, water, air, fire, the minerals, and some other such things.[7]

Such a philosophy of nature derived from a rational analysis of what he calls "certain germs of truth naturally existent in our souls" and which he drew out into a mechanics, a cosmology and a physics of the elements, has obviously little to do with the divorce between man, on the one hand, and nature and God, on the other hand, which Stob claims to find in Descartes and the philosophy of nature stemming from him.

Descartes' metaphysical dualism, then, while it may be a necessary condition, is not a sufficient condition for the dualism between man and nature adopted by the exploitive, manipulative scientists of today. The sufficient condition of the latter kind of dualism is, we maintain, Kant's radical anthropocentrism.

THE ROLE OF KANT

It was Kant who first recognized that the wedge Hume had driven between reason and experience logically jeopardized the Enlightenment's philosophy of nature. Kant saw that the orderly, lawful, rational universe seventeenth- and eighteenth-century science was disclosing to the honor of God and man had been whisked away by Hume. In its place were the essentially trivial "relations of ideas" which the perceiver's imagination supplies. Gone was any basis for the inductive inferences central to Bacon's scientific method. Equally important, the place of value in the world of fact was eliminated because the self, no less than external objects and necessary relations, was ruled out by Hume's empirical criterion of meaning.

Kant's heroic attempt to reinstate rational, moral man took the form of providing a metaphysics for Newton's physics capable of withstanding Hume's phenomenalism. To accomplish this he had to figure out how some universal, necessary propositions could be possible. He accomplished it, all right, but at a cost for which the debt is still being paid. He took the theretofore inconceivable step of redefining truth to consist not in the mind's agreement with an external object but rather in the mind's objects agreeing with the mind. The way Kant worked this novel idea out, of course, was the salvation of mathematics and physics at the expense of metaphysics. Hume proved too strong for him, for he found no way of applying the categories of the understanding to anything but spatially and temporally organized experience. The self, the world as a whole, and God became mere regulative ideas, referring to nothing. For example, speaking of God as the third idea of pure reason Kant says,

We have not the slightest ground to assume in an absolute manner (to suppose in itself) the object of this idea. . . . It becomes evident that the idea of such a being, like all speculative ideas, seeks only to formulate the command of reason, that all connection in the world be viewed in accordance with the principles of a systematic unity—as if all such connection had its source in one all-embracing being, as the supreme and all-sufficient cause. It is thus evident that reason has here no other purpose than to prescribe its own formal rule for the extension of its formal employment, and not any extension beyond all limits of empirical employment.[8]

Having failed to rescue the rational knowledge of an objective reality through science from Humean skepticism, Kant's other main goal of preserving the Enlightenment's religious and moral values could now be accomplished without regard to the conclusions of science. By limiting science to spatio-temporal experiences, he claimed to be able to affirm moral values regardless of the fact that scientifically the existence of a free, moral agent and God was nonsense.

It is this separation of scientific judgments about facts from moral judgments about values which lies behind the imposition of man's selfish values upon the world controlled by science which concerns us today.

If this be the case, then the obvious remedy of the situation is to formulate a metaphysics in which a philosophy of nature in the pre-Kantian sense be possible. That is, insights into the nature of reality must be held available and their source must be regarded as not limited to empirical science. Such a "first-order" philosophy of nature (first-order because not dependent upon current scientific theories) could justifiably, because rationally rather then empirically, intertwine scientific fact and moral values. The logical door would then be open for the kind of theology of nature which Stob has quite interestingly proposed.

Unfortunately, he jumps from the claim that Cartesian metaphysics has failed us to the construction of a theology of nature without building the philosophical framework for it on the rubble left by Hume and Kant.

RITSCHL'S VIEW OF NATURE

I find nothing wrong with Stob's theology of nature; in fact, I find much right with it. But what keeps it from being reduced to a kind of Ritschlian view of nature in reverse? Ritschl, who dominated the theological world well into the twentieth century, adopted a Kantian defense against a mechanistic, deterministic account of man with which nineteenth-century science seemed preoccupied. Realizing that man was being reduced to nature and aware that scientific positivism repudiated any claim of religious or theological knowledge about the nature of man,

Ritschl resorted to a Kantian-like postulation of a moral self over against brute nature. Such a postulation had nothing to do with scientific enquiry. Rather, he called it a value-judgment of faith, which, in turn, leads to the value-judgment of faith concerning God's existence. Just as for Kant, Ritschl's talk of God's existence or his belief in God is an expression of the value or worth God has for his moral struggle against the impersonal forces of nature. In his words,

The religious view of the world, in all its species, rests on the fact that man in some degree distinguishes himself in worth from the phenomena which surround him and from the influences of nature which press in upon him. . . . In every religion what is sought, with the help of the supernatural spiritual power reverenced by man, is a solution of the contradiction in which man finds himself, as both a part of the world of nature and a spiritual personality claiming to dominate nature. . . .

Religion springs up as faith in superhuman spiritual powers, by whose help the power which man possesses of himself is in some way supplemented, and elevated into a unity of its own kind which is a match for the pressure of the natural world. . . .

Knowledge of God can be demonstrated as religious knowledge only when he is conceived as securing to the believer such a position in the world as more than counter-balances its restrictions. Apart from this value-judgment of faith there exists no knowledge of God worthy of this content.[9]

What Ritschl is doing here is capitulating to the nineteenth-century mechanistic, deterministic philosophies of nature in the same way as Kant had assumed the validity of Newtonian physics, and then he has followed Kant's way of preserving moral man and God by making them non-rational faith postulates. Religious assertions are reduced to value judgments, leaving the factual world to the scientific method. He has denied a "first-order" philosophy of nature, that is, one which depends partially upon rational insights available prior to the constructions of empirical science. Instead, he has contented himself with a "second-order" philosophy of nature, that is, one

derived from the current theories of science, claiming no validity from extra-empirical sources.

Since for him whatever he says about nature depends upon
the validity of the science from which his statements come, he
has no alternative to viewing nature as oppressing man's spirit, if
that is what the philosophy of science (in the cosmological
sense, as distinguished from the analysis of method and meta-
language sense) of the day is saying. Then, as a substitute for
the missing first-order philosophy of nature he supplies in
Kantian fashion a theology of nature. Because he cannot episte-
mologically handle a first-order philosophy of nature, he maintains a metaphysical hiatus between his second-order philosophy of nature, dependent as it is upon the philosophy of science
of the day, on the one hand, and, on the other hand, his theology of nature, dependent as it is upon his value judgments of
faith.

The question now is whether what Stob calls his "theologico-ethical understandings" is set in a similar philosophical context. It strikes me that it tends to go in this direction because he
moves directly from claiming the source of the scientifico-technological view of nature and man to be Descartes' metaphysical
dualism to providing a theological discussion of the man-nature
problem under the headings of Creation, Fall and Redemption.

Thus we read, for example, that "Christianity knows nothing
of a dualism, unless the ontological gap which separates the
Creator from the creature be so called." Does he mean that the
truth of Christianity entails the falsity of Cartesian dualism?
Hopefully not. Then what is the logical connection between his
denial of a metaphysical dualism and his affirmation of what he
calls "the ontological gap which separates the Creator from the
creation"? Is this latter just a faith affirmation which rides free
of any metaphysics, in general, and a first-order philosophy of
nature, in particular? If so, then he has made a Ritschlian-like
separation between the first part and the second and third parts
of his paper. That is, the scientific enterprise described in the
first part as having failed to maintain a Christian stance because

of Cartesian dualism is not rebutted or corrected at that same level of discourse in the second and third parts, for there is a switch in conceptual context. Cartesian metaphysics—it could just as well be Whitehead's process philosophy or an oriental pantheism or some other monism, as is the fashion at present—is still left in charge of the philosophy of nature, with only a theological complaint registered against it. The constructive theological moves made in the second and third parts of the paper, while fine in themselves, remain to themselves in a theological world unconnected to the philosophy of nature discussed in the first part of the paper.

Hence, when Stob announces that Christianity "has broken with all intra-cosmic dualisms and monisms," we may well wonder what philosophical sense this makes.

One final but different point. It would seem to me that the most immediate philosophical antecedent of the abusive approach toward nature taken by the scientifico-technological world in which we live is existentialism, because of its pervasive influence on the thinking of the general public. The leading existentialists—Sartre, Marcel, Heidegger, etc.—developed a strong humanism in which nature was not particularly helpful in grasping the essence of man. Science, for them, is more valued for the control it affords over nature than for insights it might give into nature. The natural world is for man for the purpose of authenticating himself. This explains the leadership existentialists have offered in the attack upon the negative affects of technology on man. It also explains why the articulators of public opinion—the playwrights, artists, authors and journalists, so many of whom having been enthralled by the existentialist concern for the meaning of the self—have remained so long insensitive to the growing ecological crises.

1. *Lynn White, Jr., "The Historical Roots of Our Ecological Crises,"* Science, *March 10, 1967, p. 1205.*
2. *Ibid., p. 1206.*
3. *Ibid., p. 1207.*

4. *Kenneth Boulding,* Human Values on the Spaceship Earth *(New York: National Council of Churches, 1966), p. 14.*

5. *Ian Barbour, "Attitudes Toward Nature and Technology,"* Earth Might Be Fair, *ed. Ian Barbour (Englewood Cliffs, N.J.: Prentice-Hall, 1972), pp. 154, 156.*

6. *Montesquieu,* The Spirit of the Laws, *trans. T. Nugent, rev. ed. F. V. Prichard (Bohn: 1896-97), I, 1.*

7. *From* The Philosophical Works of Descartes, *ed. Haldane and Ross (Cambridge: Cambridge University Press, 1931), I, 121.*

8. *Immanuel Kant,* Critique of Pure Reason, *trans. N. Kemp Smith (London: Macmillan, 1929), A286=B714.*

9. *Albrecht Ritschl,* The Christian Doctrine of Justification and Reconciliation, *trans. H. R. Mackintosh and A. B. Macaulay (Edinburgh: 1900), pp. 17, 189, 212.*

II
Ethical Practice

Ethical Concerns
in Drug Research
by Hanley Abramson

During the Second World War a young Swiss scientist named Albert Hofmann was engaged in a study of some substances with central nervous system properties. In the course of these studies, he had an unusual experience, which he later described as follows:

In the afternoon of 16 April, 1943, when I was working on this problem, I was seized by a peculiar sensation of vertigo and restlessness. Objects, as well as the shape of my associates in the laboratory, appeared to undergo optical changes. I was unable to concentrate on my work. In a dream-like state I left for home where an irresistible urge to lie down overcame me. I drew the curtains and immediately fell into a drunkenness characterized by an exaggerated imagination. With my eyes closed, fantastic pictures of extraordinary plasticity and intensive color seemed to surge towards me. After two hours this state gradually wore off.

Thus it was that Hofmann, a medicinal chemist, discovered the powerful hallucinogenic effect of lysergic acid diethylamide, now better known as LSD, a minute amount of which he had unwittingly ingested during one of his experiments.

Three decades later this substance remains, for the most part, a curiosity in scientific circles, but the search into the whys and wherefores of its pronounced effects has opened up new horizons in the study of the inner workings of that most awesome of God's creations—the human mind. At the same time LSD has given us the "acid-head," symbolic of a generation of youth searching for identity and purpose.

MEDICINAL CHEMISTRY

I mentioned that Albert Hofmann was a medicinal chemist. This is also the area in which I work as an active researcher. Medicinal chemistry embodies aspects of organic chemistry, biochemistry, pharmacology and related disciplines. It seeks to discover compounds, either through chemical synthesis or isolation from natural sources, which may ultimately play roles in medical therapeutics or research. The main goal, therefore, is the design of chemical agents that may rationally be expected to cause an effect in some biological system—an effect that can be translated into practical utility for the clinician and/or researcher.

Recent decades have seen some remarkable discoveries as scientists have sought to sort out and accurately define the complex biochemical and physiological interactions that are part of man. The medicinal chemist has often successfully taken these discoveries and utilized them to design agents intended to control or alter these processes. Of course, all drugs effect these processes, but most have been discovered and developed by combinations of folklore, serendipity, hunches and "hit-and-miss" approaches. Today the art has advanced to the point where it is conceivable that the medicinal chemist could intentionally design and prepare a given compound to produce a given biological effect. Herein lie some fundamental moral and ethical decisions that must be made, particularly by the investigator who puts his faith in the Word of God.

In the realm of drug research, the ethical decision-making process may begin at the very germination of an idea. Before World War II, research was initiated on war gas materials under the impetus of the growing atmosphere of hostility prevailing in Europe. At the time, researchers felt that the issue of morality was secondary to political considerations. Incidentally, just to demonstrate the strange twists that research efforts can engender, the research that led to the development of certain nerve gases also was directly responsible for the development of some potent insecticides as well as drugs for the treatment of cancer and glaucoma. But, of course, the original research ideas were based on a negative approach as far as human ethics was concerned.

To be subject to scrutiny as an ethical or unethical concept, the research idea need not originate from such sinister motives. The move to develop orally effective contraceptive agents in the 1950s brought particularly strong reaction from the Roman Catholic Church, especially when field trials were conducted in Puerto Rico. Both researchers and clinicians of the Catholic faith were torn between scientific progress and the church in Rome, but most opted to oppose the papacy. A statement from the National Council of Churches in early 1961 declared that contraception is "morally right . . . when the motives are right" and backed up its stand with scriptural evidence. "Children are to be raised in the discipline and instruction of the Lord" (Eph. 6:4), the report declared, and for that to be true, children must have a "proper claim to parental care."

While the moral controversy regarding oral contraceptives has toned down in recent years, a new and more volatile issue has taken its place. The dispute regarding reform of present laws prohibiting abortion has had its impact on many segments of society. Some drug firms are spending millions to develop agents that will terminate pregnancy at virtually any stage. In moral terms, the question may be asked: "Does the Sixth Commandment dominate over Ephesians 6:4 in rendering the ethical decision?" I believe it does. It may be argued, and justifiably so, that these new compounds known as prostaglandins will terminate pregnancy at term and thus aid in difficult deliveries, but it cannot be denied that these substances have no competitors in causing early abortion, while there are already established drugs which aid in expulsion of the fetus at term. Their unrivaled effectiveness in producing early abortion, together with the supposition that antiabortion laws will soon be overturned, makes the prostaglandins a "hot" area for research.

INVESTIGATING BRAIN CHEMISTRY

Investigating brain chemistry is another exciting and challenging area. There are many substances, in addition to LSD, that influence brain chemistry, and these are providing science with new clues about the causes of such diseases as epilepsy and Parkinsonism and a number of psychiatric disorders, such as schizophrenia and manic depression. From such research have evolved drugs capable of managing, although not curing, some of these diseases. In addition, sedatives and tranquilizers have been introduced into medicine for the treatment of the all-too-common anxiety and tension syndrome. Names like Librium, Valium and Miltown have become household words in a society where few heed the words of Jesus: "Take my yoke upon you and learn from me; for I am gentle and lowly in heart, and you will find rest for your souls" (Mt. 11:29).

The fact that science has been able to develop mood-altering drugs, which are doubtlessly more frequently abused than correctly used, has caused some to urge that scientists ought to concentrate on providing mankind with the ultimate tranquilizer that will produce complete peace of mind. Aldous Huxley expounded that utopian dream in *Brave New World,* where the hypothetical *Soma* was used to achieve that end. While research into the drug control of certain central nervous system disorders, including mental illness, seems to me morally sound, it cannot be forgotten that chemical control of human behavior has its place only in the arena of medical therapeutics. There can be no justification for the use of mind-altering drugs as an escape from the realities of life or as political tools. Since the central theme of life is the glorification of God, the scientist who stands on Christian principles must exert his influence in society to insure that such drugs are not used in any other manner than that which is glorifying to the Creator.

The chemist from whom the research idea originates is only the starting point in a long chain of events that culminates in the introduction of a drug into general medical therapeutics. Questions of morality and ethics may crop up at any point, although the pertinent queries sometimes are not made until tragedy demands it. Many years ago Elixir Sulfanilamide was marketed when some scientists found a good solvent for this difficultly soluble new wonder drug. Failure to realize the extreme toxicity of this solvent caused many deaths and a tightening of federal control over drugs. This control helped the United States to avert disaster when thalidomide came on the scene. A recent development in drug control is the discovery that many drugs and drug combinations introduced in the last twenty-five years are inefficacious. Scientists, clinicians and federal administrators have at last begun to tackle the moral issue of whether or not the public should be endangered by the presence of prescription drug products that really do not accomplish what is claimed for them.

Drug toxicity is also a matter for concern. Toxicity is, of course, a relative word. Is a drug that will cause fatal liver damage in one patient out of 10,000 a toxic agent? To 9,999 individuals it may be completely safe, but to that one patient it makes a world of difference. Is it moral for a drug company to continue marketing a drug product when it knows full well that, say, ten individuals will die during the next year because they used that drug? The question can be put into a different light by asking, Is it moral to deprive countless people of the benefits of a particular drug on the basis that a very small percentage of the population will die or suffer debilitating side effects as a result of taking that drug?

USING DRUGS IN HEALTH CARE
Such a question must be examined in the broad scope of health care. A new medicinal agent, even though proven effective and relatively safe in clinical trials under controlled conditions, can and often does present a multitude of problems when used in general therapeutics. Not the least of these problems is the actual manner in which it is utilized by the physician. The drug regimen prescribed for a given patient must be compatible with certain criteria for that patient. Among these are diagnosis, pre-

vious medical history, complicating conditions, sensitivities, etc. For example, a particular drug may be perfectly satisfactory in a cardiac patient with no complicating conditions whereas use of the same drug in a cardiac patient with a history of gout necessitates some additional considerations. Adequate follow-up of the patient is also required so that drug-induced conditions can be detected before serious damage to the individual ensues.

Obviously, few if any physicians today are able to keep abreast of all pertinent information on drugs emanating from laboratories and health-care institutions throughout the world, nor are they able to provide each patient with an optimum therapeutic regimen and follow-up. This burden must be taken up by other health professionals. In my role as a pharmacy educator, as well as a medicinal chemistry researcher, I have the obligation of training future pharmacy practitioners who will be so completely versed in drug effects as to be able to advise the physician along these lines. This newly emerging role for the pharmacist goes far beyond the moral obligations traditionally conceived by the profession.

Although a new drug may be subjected to countless animal experiments, valid data for that drug can be obtained only through clinical trials. If a new agent of unknown value is placed in clinical trials with patients whose conditions could possibly be benefited by it, is it ethical to assign some of these patients to a placebo group? Without question, to conduct such a trial in an uncontrolled fashion would definitely be unethical, since no valid information would be obtained.

No investigator has an inherent right to conduct experiments on other human beings, regardless of the potential benefits to humanity. In every experiment the informed consent of the subject (or guardian) must be secured. The subject must be thoroughly apprised of the testing procedure, which is frequently "double-blind" (that is, neither the subject nor the person administering the agent is aware of whether the administered substance is the drug on trial or a placebo). This procedure was followed in the 1954 field trials of the Salk polio vaccine, except, of course, that parents had to give the consent for their children. It is obvious that a certain number of children contracted polio and died as a result of receiving the placebo instead of the vaccine. But the risk to the control group was not greater than before the trial of the vaccine, which had potential hazards of its own; and the controlled trial was the only way to determine whether or not the vaccine was effective.

No patient may justifiably be denied the benefits of the best treatment available. Certainly, therefore, placebo controls are not permissible if an effective drug is already known. Therefore, any new drug must be evaluated in a comparative trial against the best existing one.

A most important area for concern is the effect of a new drug on the human fetus when administered to a pregnant patient. The thalidomide experience has taught us that good judgment must be exercised in prescribing drugs in pregnancy. Deliberate experimentation with drugs to determine their effects on the fetus is transparently unethical and most clues as to which drugs should be avoided in pregnancy, if at all obtainable, are secured from animal experiments. Yet there are cases where drugs must be used in pregnancy since both mother and fetus may be at greater risk without drug therapy. In these situations retrospective analyses have given the physician valuable information regarding the use of many drugs in pregnancy without putting either mother or fetus at greater risk than was already present.

It has often been stated that the fruits of drug research have served to change human morality. Oral contraceptives, it is claimed, have ushered in a new era of sexual freedom. Prostaglandins allow us to conveniently deprive a fetus of life. Heroin and other addictive and habituating agents have become an integral part of the lives of many of our citizens. Perhaps it is more correct to state that the ready availability of certain kinds of drug products have intensified and made more dramatic the base of sinful behavior that is part of the individual whose life has no room for the Lord Jesus. A drug can be as much a tool of divine healing as of demonic dealing. As professionals and citizens, we must do our part to emphasize the former and dispose of the latter.

Is the Scientist for Hire?
by John A. McIntyre

The title for this essay has been selected to introduce an issue that has recently captured the attention of the scientific community: "What are the social responsibilities of scientists?" Can a scientist pursue his profession without considering the effects of his work on the welfare of other men and on society?

In the past, the scientist has usually done his work in isolation from worldly affairs. Thus, the tradition developed that the scientist is a disinterested "seeker after truth." The scientist in ordinary circumstances gave little heed to the use society might make of the results of his work. Physicists, for example, expressed their devotion to this disengagement from worldly affairs in the following words in the Constitution of the American Physical Society: "The object of the Society shall be the advancement and diffusion of the knowledge of physics."[1]

However, in the last five years or so a significant part of the physics community has begun to criticize the traditional way of doing things. The use of advanced technology in the Vietnam War has no doubt had a strong influence on this re-evaluation of the role of physicists in society. Since many physicists have opposed the war, the question of the utilization of new physical discoveries by the government has become acutely relevant. Critics have attacked physicists doing classified work on the grounds that such work is in conflict with the purpose of the American Physical Society to "diffuse the knowledge of physics."

As a result of this situation, an amendment to the Constitution of the American Physical Society has been presented to the
Society's membership. While the present constitution restricts
itself to the words, "the object of the Society shall be the
advancement and diffusion of the knowledge of physics," the
amendment adds the following, "in order to increase man's
understanding of nature and to contribute to the enhancement
of the quality of life for all people. The society shall assist its
members in the pursuit of these humane goals and it shall shun
those activities which are judged to contribute harmfully to the
welfare of mankind."

In this amendment we have an expression of the broader view
that the scientist cannot fulfill his obligations merely by finding
new knowledge and transmitting this new knowledge; rather,
the physics profession must decide whether the new knowledge
should be disseminated or even whether the scientist should
investigate certain parts of nature.

THE EXPERIENCE OF THE LEGAL PROFESSION

While contemplating these various factors, it occurred to me
that the rather young scientific profession might learn something from the two ancient professions of medicine and law.
These professions have established standards of professional
ethics which have survived the rise and fall of civilizations. What
are the responsibilities of the members of these two professions?

For application to the scientific profession it appeared to me
that the standards of the legal profession would be more pertinent. The lawyer deals not only with people but also with
corporations and the government. His actions and advice can be
used by his employers for purposes over which he has no control. What does the American Bar Association say about the
responsibility of lawyers in these circumstances?

An important feature of the relationship between the client
and his counsel is the trust that the client must be able to

repose in his counsel. The American Bar Association expresses the importance of this trust in these words:

The purposes and necessities of the relation between a client and his attorney require, in many cases, on the part of the client, the fullest and freest disclosures to the attorney of the client's objects, motives, and acts. This disclosure is made in the strictest confidence, relying upon the attorney's honor and fidelity. To permit the attorney to reveal to others what is so disclosed, would be not only a gross violation of a sacred trust upon his part, but it would utterly destroy and prevent the usefulness and benefits to be derived from professional assistance. Based upon considerations of public policy, therefore, the law wisely declares that all confidential communications and disclosures, made by a client to his legal advisor for the purpose of obtaining his professional aid or advice, shall be strictly privileged;—that the attorney shall not be permitted, without the consent of his client,—and much less will he be compelled—to reveal or disclose communications made to him under such circumstances.

The lawyer must decide when he takes a case whether it is a suitable one for him to undertake and after this decision is made, he is not justified in turning against his client by exposing injurious evidence entrusted to him. . . . [D]oing something intrinsically regrettable, because the only alternative involves worse consequences, is a necessity in every profession.[2]

To dramatize these procedures, one could imagine a lawyer working for the Mafia. The lawyer could not, because of his professional relationship, ethically reveal illegal acts of the Mafia of which he had knowledge. Furthermore, in spite of his distaste for the client's character or actions, the lawyer would have to be zealous in using every ethical means to defend his client. That there may be personal tensions for the lawyer under such circumstances is undeniable, but they must be accepted as part of his professional responsibility. A sympathetic expression of this professional problem is given by the American Bar Association:

The traditional position of the American bar has been that a lawyer may apply his personal views of his client's morality only in a limited degree and only in deciding whether to accept the case in the first instance. He is never required to perform any act which violates his own conscience, but his role as advocate permits and requires that he press all points legally available even if he must subordinate his personal evaluation of his client's conduct. His private belief that one ought to answer fully any question asked must yield to his role as counsel; as counsel he is prevented from disclosing what he has learned in confidence from his client. He may personally believe that certain rules of law which benefit his client are wrong and ought to be changed, but it is his obligation in the course of representation to invoke them on his client's behalf. [3]

In summary, then, a lawyer's first duty is to his client. He is not allowed by the ethics of his profession to sacrifice his client's interests even though they may conflict with the interests of innocent third parties.

The English and the American bars agree concerning another important issue—the responsibility of lawyers to respond to requests for legal assistance:

In England every barrister holds himself out as ready to undertake any case, regardless of its type, which requires his appearance in court, subject only to the availability of his time and arrangements for an appropriate fee. . . . The highest tradition of the American bar is found in the obligation of the lawyer's oath never to reject "from any consideration personal to myself, the cause of the defenseless or oppressed." A lawyer has the duty to provide legal assistance "even to the most unpopular defendants. . . ." The great tradition of the bar is reflected in the history of eminent lawyers—from John Adams' defense of British "Redcoats" charged after the so-called Boston Massacre to the present day—who have risked public disfavor to defend a hated defendant. [4]

This insistence that the legal profession must make itself available to all men is based on the fact that all men have a right to a fair trial and that a fair trial is not possible without the defendant having legal counsel.[5]

SCIENTISTS AND LEGAL ETHICS

If the scientist is a professional, as will be assumed in the following, his first obligation in any employment situation is also to his client, or employer. That this obligation may include not publishing his scientific results is to be expected. For years, scientists in corporations have withheld proprietary information, if only to file patents. To say that the purpose of the American Physical Society to diffuse scientific information (by supporting journals, for example) prohibits the physicist from doing classified work is to confuse the purpose of the society with the professional responsibilities of its members. It makes no difference, of course, if the employer is the United States Government.

But is the professional responsible for the actions of his client or employer? The position of the legal profession is clear. When acting in his official capacity (and here the wearing of the wig in the British courtroom reveals its significance), the professional restricts his actions and responsibilities to those required by his office. The character and former actions of the defendant are irrelevant to the business at hand, as are the possible consequences of the decision to be made, except insofar as they bear on the issue before the court. Thus, a member of the Mafia may be acquitted even though the social consequences may be frightening.

The same ethic guides all professions. A doctor would conscientiously treat Adolph Hitler even though he was convinced that the death of this one man would save many innocent lives from the gas chambers. A priest would also maintain the confidence of the confessional under all circumstances. There is no question that these ethics are sound. If one were lying ill, it would be a terrible thing to watch the attending physician mentally deciding whether one's recovery would "contribute harmfully to the welfare of mankind," to use the wording of the proposed amendment to the Constitution of the American Physical Society.

One therefore reaches the conclusion that, while functioning in his professional capacity, the professional in any field has only a professional responsibility to his client and not a social responsibility. Thus, insofar as a scientist is acting in this professional capacity, the phrase "the social responsibility of scientists" is a contradiction in terms, and to bring social factors into a code of professional ethics is mischievous and confusing.

The lawyer is available to all—Angela Davis, the Mafia and even the Defense Department. The fact that some of these clients may be unpopular in the eyes of the community because their actions may appear to "contribute harmfully to the welfare of mankind" is even more reason for the lawyer to make his services available. By analogy, then, the scientist should make himself available to all those who desire his services, regardless of whether their actions "contribute harmfully to the welfare of mankind."

However, this simple application of legal ethics to the scientific situation is too careless. There is an additional factor involved in the legal relationships, the court. In the matter under consideration, the court is a source of support for the client, a support to which the client has a right of access. The insistence that the lawyer make his services available is based on the fact that without legal services the client will forfeit his right to appear in court. This right of the client exists independently of his moral character and is the basis for the responsibility of the legal profession to make counsel available.

Therefore, if the legal procedures are to be applied to the scientific milieu, it is necessary to find some feature in the scientific situation that corresponds to the court in the legal situation. This source of support must be such that the scientist's client, the Defense Department for example, (1) has a right of access to the source and (2) requires the services of a scientist to exercise this right. Is there such a source of support?

Traditionally, there has been a source to which the Defense

Department has had a right to appeal. This source is the American people, and the support which they supply consists of military weapons. Expressed in political terms, it is the determination that if American soldiers are to be required to risk their lives in the service of their country their fellow citizens will provide them with the equipment to protect them during this service. So, just as the accused person has a right to a fair trial, the American soldier through the Defense Department has a right to proper military support.

It is at this point, then, that scientists, as professionals, are required to protect the rights of a class of citizens, in this case the soldiers. Without the scientists' contributions to the improvement of weapons, the soldier would be exposed to dangers from which he would otherwise be protected. It is on this ground that the Defense Department can expect the scientific profession to make its members available for employment.

As already discussed, this employment is required even if the employer can be criticized for some of his actions. The scientist can and should refuse, though, to participate himself in actions which he discerns to be immoral or unethical. Thus, he should not cooperate in the construction of a weapon that is outlawed by the conventions of war. He would, however, be obliged to participate in the construction of a weapon which he believes should be outlawed if the weapon is still a legal one. He is then in the position of a lawyer who must use an undesirable law to defend his client.

Furthermore, every scientist is not required to work for the Defense Department. Just as one would not expect a Jewish lawyer to defend the Nazis in the war crimes trials, so one would not expect those strongly opposed to the Vietnam War to be effective employees of the Defense Department. Nevertheless, some lawyers had to defend the Nazis, and the position of the bar would be to encourage these lawyers in their work. Similarly, the American Physical Society should take the position of encouraging physicists to work for the Defense Department.

THE CHRISTIAN VIEW OF RESPONSIBILITY

So far our discussion has been based on the distilled experience of one of the great professions. Nonetheless, we will now show that the conclusions reached are remarkably in accord with Christian teaching.

Perhaps the most direct teaching about responsibility is Jesus' response to the Jews' question about paying taxes. Jesus' reply, "Render, therefore, to Caesar the things that are Caesar's, and to God the things that are God's,"[6] shows that Jesus supported the state with his taxes, even though the state, as any human institution, is not always moral in its behavior. Because Jesus also claimed to be sinless,[7] it is clear that he did not hold himself accountable for the immoral actions of the state.

Other examples of this same attitude are Peter's and Paul's admonitions to Christians to obey the state.[8] Also, when soldiers asked John the Baptist what they should do to bear fruit that befits repentance, he said, "Rob no one by violence or by false accusation, and be content with your wages."[9] This is a perfect example of limiting the responsibility of an employee to performing his duties in a moral manner; there is no indication that the soldiers should repent of the policy of the army in which they served.

Even when describing the church as the body of Christ, Paul uses a metaphor which conveys that individual Christians are independently responsible only for their own functions.[10] Clearly the eye can have no control or responsibility for the foot. Only the head, Jesus Christ, and those to whom he has delegated his authority, are responsible for the actions of the church, although the individual member is clearly responsible for seeing that his part of the body functions satisfactorily.

This obedience to human authority is not unlimited, however. In Jesus' teaching on taxes, obedience to Caesar is not the only consideration. Thus, when Peter and John were ordered by the authorities to desist from preaching the gospel, they replied, "Whether it is right in the sight of God to listen to you rather than to God, you must judge; for we cannot but speak of what we have seen and heard."[11] This Christian insistence on Caesar's deferring to God is paralleled, of course, in the legal situation where the lawyer is not required to act against his conscience.

In summary, then, the Bible teaches consistently that in social groups a man's responsibility is restricted to his own actions. In performing these actions a man defers to human authority unless such authority demands actions opposing the laws of God.

DO SCIENTISTS HAVE SOCIAL RESPONSIBILITIES?

Perhaps the preceding discussion has led some to the conclusion that scientists do not have responsibilities to society. Such a conclusion is erroneous. Of course, scientists have responsibilities, as do all citizens. And, indeed, their scientific training may equip them to discharge some responsibilities with particular effectiveness.

What has been said before is that in his role of a professional, the scientist does not have social responsibilities; rather, he has professional responsibilities. Thus, a science professor in his professional role in the classroom will not promote political candidates. However, at a political meeting, with perhaps the same students in the audience, he might very well support certain candidates. Sometimes the public does not understand these distinctions, but certainly the professional should. Perhaps we should begin to wear wigs at the appropriate times.

In fact, then, the social responsibilities of a professional are hardly restricted. And, because of his professional knowledge, he has a greater responsibility in some areas than the ordinary citizen. Significantly, the legal profession recognizes this responsibility in the following words: "Lawyers often serve as legislators or as holders of other public offices. This is highly desirable as lawyers are uniquely qualified to make significant contributions to the improvement of the legal system. . . ."[12]

Scientists can easily find and have often found opportunities to influence social and political affairs. They will continue to do so while at the same time they faithfully discharge their professional duties.

SUMMARY

1. The scientist's primary responsibility is to his client or employer. Because of this responsibility he must not violate the trust placed in him not to divulge any information which he has received in confidence. Thus, classified work is proper for a scientist.

2. The scientist is not responsible for the actions of his client or employer. Thus, he may, by ethically assisting his employer, actually be impairing the welfare of mankind. As a professional, however, he will refuse to participate in unethical activities such as writing false reports. He will also refuse personally to participate in the illegal activities of his employer.

3. The scientific profession has a responsibility to provide scientists for those with a "right" to such professional service. The Defense Department, for one, has such a right on the grounds that the American soldier has a right to be properly equipped. Other persons or organizations may also have a "right" to scientific support. Such other persons have not been considered in this paper.

4. None of the above conclusions is to be construed as implying that scientists do not have responsibilities to society when not serving in their professional capacities.

Returning now to the proposed amendment to the Constitution of the American Physical Society, we conclude that:

5. As a professional society, the American Physical Society should restrict its concern to the professional activities of its members.

6. Since the professional activities have been shown to be independent of the welfare of mankind, it is improper to introduce such phraseology into the Constitution's statement of purpose.

---

1. Bulletin of the American Physical Society, *Series II, Vol. 17 (1972), p. 737.*

2. *American Bar Association Code of Professional Responsibility and Canons of Judicial Ethics, Canon 4, footnotes 1 and 4.*

3. *Standards Relating to the Prosecution Function and the Defense Function. Recommended March, 1970, by the Advisory Committee on the Prosecution and Defense Functions of the American Bar Association Project on Standards for Criminal Justice, pp. 148-49.*

4. *Ibid., pp. 188-89.*

5. *American Bar Association Code, EC 7-1.*

6. *Matthew 22:21.*

7. *John 8:46.*

8. *1 Peter 2:13-17 and Romans 13:1-7.*

9. *Luke 3:13.*

10. *1 Corinthians 12.*

11. *Acts 4:19-20.*

12. *Standards Relating to the Prosecution Function, EC 8-8.*

Language and Self Image
by Kenneth L. Pike

I n Judaic and Christian terms, man in some sense finds himself in the image of God, by the initiative of God. Part of this image includes the fact that man is verbal, and can talk to himself. His ability to talk to himself, to argue with himself, to propose lines of activity, tentatively, before embarking upon them, is a crucial part of his selfhood. Without it he would not be man.

To me, as a linguist, it seems extraordinary that it is precisely in the area of language that science can study directly, by its full scientific apparatus, one component—a communicative system—where man shares a characteristic with God. We affirm that there cannot be complete discontinuity between the two communication systems, or else relations of communication between God and man would be severed. The affirmation here, for the Christian linguist, is not that the language of God and man is identical, nor comparable in degree, but rather that there is sufficient overlap in design to allow for communication between them.

God's image of himself is that of a Being who can *talk*—to himself, and to us—and can *choose* to talk. In representing himself to us as the Self-Revealing One, he tells us in John: "In the beginning was the Word." And to a linguist, a startling characteristic of this crucial part of the Scriptures is its linguistic metaphor. Similarly, in the assertion of God's ultimate responsibility for the presence of the world, there is a linguistic link: "And God said, 'Let us . . .' and 'Let there be. ... .' " Here the tacit affirmation of the linguistic competence of God sets up the implication of God's self awareness as related to his ability to communicate with himself and with his creation.

If this affirmation is false, then Christianity, Judaism and Islam all disintegrate. Pantheism, with God as part of a tree, tree as part of man, and all merged into one immense smearing wholeness, replaces the concept of the One who can say "I" and "you." Eventually, every permanent self image disappears under this attack, whether it be through mysticism in the East or materialism in the West. In the East, the contrastive self images can disappear into a singleness of mystic spirit, so that, for Hinduism, "to attain salvation was to realize absorption into the Brahma Atman, where the changing world of daily living was illusion";[1] and "the Buddha taught the doctrine of Impermanence and Non-Ego. He declared that both the self and things were only compounds of elements and, as such, had no permanent identity."[2]

In the West, however, a mechanistic view can equally destroy the possibility of a choice-capacity prerequisite to the relevant affirmation of the existence of truth or falsehood, or of any ethic involving belief in some factor other than physical events and things. Leslie A. White, a vigorous cultural determinist (and formerly a colleague of mine in the Anthropology Department at the University of Michigan) says: "Whether a man—an average man, typical of his group—believes in Christ or Buddha, Genesis or Geology, Determinism or Free Will, is not a matter of his own choosing. His philosophy is merely the response of his neuro-sensory-muscular-glandular system to the streams of cultural stimuli impinging upon him from the outside."[3]

It has always seemed to me that a weak point in this position was precisely the fact that he bothered to write the book. There is implied, I feel, the belief that in this particular case the book's affirmations have a validity outside of the author's biography, glands and environment—a position not allowed by the book itself. B. F. Skinner mentions this problem as raised by his own brand of materialism: "I have had my lecture. I have no sense of fatherhood. If my genetic and personal histories had been different, I should have come into a possession of a different lecture." He claims only to have "served as a place in which certain processes could take place."[4] In fact, in the same article, Skinner states that in the days when he was writing his *Verbal Behavior,* he "thought it was possible to account for verbal behavior in terms of the history of the speaker, without reference to ideas, meanings, propositions, and the like."[5] So that the poet, also, is "having" a poem, like having a baby.

A verbal component enters the discussion: If a person has no choice, this certainly applies to choice of words. But if choice is an illusion, why should a person write a book affirming that it is true that there is no choice to write a book? If one's choice to believe in Christ or Buddha is totally determined, so is one's choice to believe in determinism—and hence a book on the subject becomes irrelevant as a verbal document, since it may have been written merely because of some reinforcement which does not have any necessary connection with truth or social value or logical support of a position. In my view, Skinner thus destroys the validity of his evident belief in the value of his conclusions; and this type of linguistic legerdemain, concealing the source of his self-confidence as to the possibility of recognizing *any* truth, then contaminates his views of responsible behavior—and of any potential ethics growing out of it. One's view of ethics, I maintain, has as a component a view of responsibility in the use of language. Loss of the one entails loss of the other. Hence, as linguist, I am interested in the problem.

It is interesting to see that White (in the volume mentioned above), when attempting to pinpoint the difference between man and animals, seems to use verbal creativity as some kind of free choice: "The man differs from the dog—and all other creatures—in that he *can and does play an active role in determining what value the vocal stimulus is to have, and the dog cannot*" (italics in the original). And, "This creative faculty, that of freely, actively, and arbitrarily bestowing value upon things, is one of the most commonplace as well as *the* most important characteristic of man. Children employ it freely in their play: 'Let's pretend that this rock is a wolf.' " And, "All *human* existence depends upon it and it alone."[6]

Man is, indeed, a creator. He can invent sonnets, novels or mundane sentences not heard before. And it was in this connection that a devastating attack upon the work of B. F. Skinner came from a linguist, Noam Chomsky,[7] who continues to assert[8] that "the normal use of language is not only innovative and potentially infinite in scope, but second, also free from control of detectable stimuli, either external or internal. It is because of this freedom from stimulus-control that language can serve as an instrument of thought and self-expression, as it does not only for the exceptionally gifted and talented, but, in fact, for every normal human being.[9]

LEARNING FROM ONE'S ADVERSARIES
But now an ethical problem, for the scientist, arises from a rejection of the underlying philosophy of behaviorism: Can he learn from such people? And can he encourage his students to learn from them, profitably and sympathetically? Here I answer vigorously, "Yes." We have a strong ethical obligation to learn from people who disagree with us, and even from people who might conceivably treat our philosophical—or scientific—views with contempt.

It is an ethical obligation on the scientist who is a theist to act upon the implications of his own finiteness, and the evident choice of God to send scientific rain—scientific insight—on the just and on the unjust. All of our models are partial. All are therefore in need of insights of other—also partial—models. And we must have the initiative and character to search for aspects in other models which will be helpful antidotes to our own hyperboles. As for myself, I am indebted to mechanists in numerous ways, and delighted to acknowledge that debt.

To Leslie White I owe, for instance, much greater understanding of the importance of independent invention of ideas, and deeper insight into the conditioning of people. His work suggests—to me, not to him—what may be some of the driving mechanism implementing the fact that God visits the iniquities of some of the fathers upon their children to the third and fourth generation (Ex. 20:5); and I suspect that Skinner has been allowed by God to see some aspects of this same truth— distorted, in my view, by his hyperbole which leaves no tiny room for some crucial final flip points in choice or in the normal writing of a poem. In addition, as I have written elsewhere,[10] Christian linguists can and do use profitably the various current major theories—as I have profited immensely, in preparing people for Bible translation, from the earlier mechanistic work of Bloomfield.[11] Similarly, just two days ago a social worker in the schools of neighboring Ypsilanti told me how she was getting helpful results in aiding disturbed black children to integrate more effectively into the classroom situation—and the stimulus for the practical techniques was in part derived from Skinner.

Thus, while I am deeply sympathetic with the philosophical objections of Francis A. Schaeffer to Skinner, I feel we must object to his implication that any patterned drill is behavioristic and that any such teaching should lead us to abandon academic involvement and cooperation at the university level. He says, "Aren't pattern drills in the language lab always behavioristic, and even when these are helpful don't they support Harris's warning that Skinner must be taken seriously because 'he has a program and followers to push it'? A brilliant young girl in a social science department in a British university was forced to choose to teach on a behavioristic level or to leave the university. The girl walked out. She had to."[12]

AN ETHICAL PROBLEM ARISING FROM LANGUAGE

The individual becomes aware, in part, of his relation to a particular social stratum or group by the way he talks. His pronunciation identifies him with the larger structure. It is by no petty accident of history that the difference between "shibboleth" and "sibboleth" (Judg. 12:6) was a life-and-death matter ("he

could not frame to pronounce it right"—so off with his head).
Rather, group identity was labelled by the difference.

Yet language-based identity goes far deeper and penetrates to
the very heart of one's freedom to be a man. Recently, for
example, I was talking with a scholar who appeared to me in
every sense to be a normal native speaker of English. I suspected
nothing otherwise. In the conversation, however, it turned out
that he was a Dane, and he bristled when a hypothetical situation was mentioned in which small nations might learn the language of larger nations rather than retaining their own. He explained to me that in spite of his fluency in English, and his
professional competence, there were many areas in which he
could use only Danish—that "his *full freedom* was *only* in his
mother tongue." Self image, freedom, identity and responsibility tie together in language.

It is only in relation to some such explanation—or a fuller
one—that I can understand a bit of the insistence of some
minority communities at retaining their own languages in spite
of massive pressures from a dominant culture. I have heard
scholars from such languages, for example, insist that they have
had their moral structure built inseparably from their mother
tongue—and they insist, tenaciously, that they must maintain it.
Some time ago, for example, there were with us for dinner three
women, each from a different but small country in Europe.
Each had her professional training and career tied either closely
or exclusively to English. Yet when asked which of their numerous languages (all were multi-lingual) they would retain, if they
could keep only one, each affirmed that it would be her mother
tongue.

On the other hand, if a person feels that it is a disadvantage
for him to belong to a particular group, he may attempt to
change his group by changing his language. Specifically, this
kind of drive may lead a person to learn the language of his
conquerors—to get a job at court, to speak in the fashion of the
court, to become a part of the dominant group.

When people wish to change their language or social dialect in order to have for themselves or their children opportunities of a type they consider valuable, it would seem ethically proper to help them to do so. Yet even in the very process of being helpful, ethical distortion may enter. Many persons, for example, have wanted to teach black students standard English in order to make them acceptable on the job market at a higher social or economic level. A great deal of effort has recently gone into discussing this possibility. But it is quite possible to view this effort at being helpful as a perversion of ethics, if it is carried on in such a way that it persuades people that their own language is in some sense inferior, and destroys their valuable, necessary self-confidence to an appreciable degree. From the linguistic point of view, there is no absolute scale of good and bad in language for such purposes.

The very attempt to be helpful can appear to accuse people of an innate inferiority when in fact the differences of language are due to irrelevant historical events or accident. Under these circumstances, a program of our government which can appear to be good can be in practice damaging. Consider, for example, the following quotation from James Sledd of the University of Texas:

The immorality of that effort is the chief reason why enforced bi-dialectalism should not be tolerated even if it were possible. Predators can and do use dialect differences to exploit and oppress, because ordinary people can be made to doubt their own value and to accept subservience if they can be made to despise the speech of their fathers. Obligatory bi-dialectalism for minorities is only another mode of exploitation, another way of making blacks behave as whites would like them to. It is unnecessary for communication. . . . Its psychological consequences are likely to be nervous affectation, self-distrust, dislike for everyone not equally afflicted with the itch to get ahead, and eventual frustration by the discovery that the reward for so much suffering is intolerably small. At best the altered student will get a somewhat better job and will move up a few places in the rat-race of the underlings. At worst he will be cut off from

*other blacks, still not accepted among whites, and economically
no better off than he was before.*[13]
The more one senses that language and self image are related,
the more forceful these ethical problems may become when one
is dealing with language minorities.

THE ETHICS OF USING LANGUAGE FOR RESEARCH
In the last two years there has been extensive controversy in the
American Anthropological Association regarding the nature of
ethics necessary for the profession of anthropology. Growing
out of this debate has come a presentation of the philosophy
for such an ethic by Joseph G. Jorgensen of the University of
Michigan.[14] He insists that an ethical code cannot be based on
scientific principles (322b, 325a); "a normative ethic for an-
thropologists can be based only on the understanding we develop from our experiences in human encounters." He is insistent
that "we are bound by the informant's claim to the right of
privacy and by the commitment we make as an inducement to
gain his cooperation. We are *ethically* bound to honor that commitment" (327b). So he treats ethical questions of privacy, consent and confidentiality: "We are doubly obligated to spell out
our intentions and not to exploit their naïveté" (328a); and, "it
is unethical for an anthropologist to disguise his identity in
order to enter a private domain, to lie about the character of
the research he is conducting, or to allow the data he has collected to be used for purposes he does not understand but
which he has reason to believe can cause harm to his infor-
mants" (330b).
   Since several of my present and former colleagues in anthropology at the University of Michigan—including Jorgensen—have
been deeply involved in this debate, I have followed it with
interest. By September of 1970, information given by candidates for office in the American Anthropological Association
revolved heavily around their attitudes towards the "potentially
devisive problems of ethics" and "the impossibility of value
freedom and political neutrality in our world."[15] The very sur-

vival of the Association and its legitimacy were represented as dependent upon the solutions to these matters.

In March of 1970 members Wolf and Jorgensen of the Ethics Committee of the Association were given[16] a series of purloined documents discussing the situation in Thailand, which the committee felt "contradicted in spirit and in letter the resolutions of the American Anthropological Association, concerning clandestine and secret research." The discussion continued in further Newsletters: 11.8.1-2, 8, 12; 11.2.7-15. By the latter, the annual report of the Committee on Ethics is given, with proposals for a statement of professional responsibility—an explicit statement (11) that "these documents we obtained, ie, xeroxed without permission from the files of an anthropologist prominently mentioned in them by a graduate student research assistant." Material continued: 11.10.2, 10-11; 12.1.2, 7-13, 15-20 (with extensive reply by two of the persons accused); 12.2.9; 12.3.1-2, 6-7, 9-13; 12.4.7; 12.5.2; 13.1.1 (an ad hoc committee's report rejected by the Council), 3-4, 9; 13.2.1, 6 (the Board affirms that the "Thailand controversy" stands unresolved).

Is it ethical to use language to change people at all? If not, then all educators should go out of business, and no one should be allowed to write a book. Yet if we assume that it is, in fact, sometimes ethical to change people by use of language, then we have to ask what ethical constraints there should be on this use of language to obtain research data or to pass it on.

OUR CHARACTER SEEN THROUGH OUR LANGUAGE

Our use of language is an index to our character. What we say allows others to see what we are. Yet such a statement appears to be a hyperbole, since people are sometimes able to conceal the fact they are lying, deliberately distorting the truth. It is especially, therefore, during the times when our words are uttered without careful control that language, as a character index, can best be read. Perhaps for this reason it is appropriate that man must give account, in the final judgment, for "every idle word" (Mt. 12:36).

I have attempted to suggest how this in fact works in a social situation by referring to the language of Peter at the time of his betrayal of Christ: It was his local, "hillbilly" dialect that identified him to the onlookers, as my poem attempts to emphasize.[17] Voice quality is shown by marginal comments. Crescendo, decrescendo and stresses are shown by crescendo marks and accent marks over the words; the continuous line represents the pitch of the voice (high directly over the letters; mid pitch directly under the letters; extra high level and extra low level above and below the words, respectively). It is characteristics such as these, fully as much as the words themselves, which betray one's inner attitudes toward the content of what he is saying, toward his audience and toward himself. These characteristics are not easy to conceal—though they can be handled, except for idle moments, in a "dead-pan voice."

Verbal control of our expressive capacities, it seems to me, has a curious feedback on freedom. If we curse our enemies—or those who despitefully use us—a habit can set in. If *each time* someone bothers us we allow that environment to evoke from us an angry reply (or behavior intended to damage others), then eventually the environment is controlling our major reaction energy. There is so much to make a person angry (directly or in memory) that his actions could end up being almost fully determined by an annoying environment. He has, in fact, become a slave to the environment. He has lost his freedom, with his actions dictated by evil from outside him. In the process of this reacting, he may also have lost his personal dignity in the view of others.

Curiously enough, therefore, both freedom and dignity demand that one does not return insult for insult. Freedom requires that one bless those who persecute him and that he be both kindly and pleasant to those who are unkindly and unpleasant to him. Freedom requires that a person verbally, and in non-verbal behavior, build a self image which does not require him to repay evil with evil.

Thy Speech Betrayeth Thee

Relaxed, soft   *Hów* can I tell who you áre?

Slow, caustic   Every *idle-wórd*

     márks your tráck

     with prívate scént.

Speed up   Every vówel, évery tóne, évery 'R',

     gives a tráce of your órigin

     and your bént from afár.

Faster, with staccato stress-groups (= early decrescendo)   Clues to crónies and your wórks

     are wrapped up in áccent chírps

     Líttle Bírd!

     Dòn't you trý to flý—

     just den`́`y

     and skwáwk and crý

Slow down; stress and lengthen first word   (ànd be prepáred to díe)

     Little Bírd.

Fast Staccato   Character will óut

     just as sóftly

     and as lóudly

     as you shóut;

Relaxed   or póut.

Resulting from this is a character which is like the character of God, who sends rain upon the just and the unjust. (See Mt. 5:43-48.) God is able to act on his own initiative without his actions being purely reaction against something else. Therefore when in unfavorable circumstances we also act, by our own choice, to be good, we have entered into part of the character of God.

The tongue is a rudder (Jas. 3:5-12). And only by the prior choice of self control of the tongue can one steer oneself toward freedom from control of self by an evil environment. Even the captivity to his environment of a good man, like Job, may not be eased until he prays for friends who have badgered him. A choice of positive verbal action, painfully taken, utilizing what small degree of individual freedom for choice in fact adheres to us by the grace of God, is necessary to fulfill one condition for obtaining part of that freedom which is at the heart of God.

Skinner has said, "It is in the nature of an experimental analysis of human behavior that it should strip away the functions previously assigned to autonomous man and transfer them one by one to the controlling environment."[18] If we rephrase this to state that one effect of evil is that it in fact strips away from man, one by one, functions of choice and assigns them to an environment, we can then see why Christ insists that one greet one's enemies in a friendly way and pray for those who despitefully use him. This is precisely the reverse of outside conditioning: It restores to man one by one the freedoms of his inner action—despite environmental conditions which impinge upon him. Such people know the truth, react to it with mercy, and the truth makes them free. Thus the ethics of the use of language require that one does not damage others. The Christian ethic, however, goes far beyond the negative requirement not to damage; it requires that—in the face of damage—one bless and pray for the opposition. This turns out to be costly in human dignity for the moment, but with a very great long-range payoff in terms of internal freedom and value to the community.

Self image must involve one's own assessment of how he wishes to use language.

1. *E. J. J., "Hinduism,"* Collier's Encyclopedia *(New York and Toronto: P. F. Collier and Son, 1959), X, 69a.*

2. *W. T. C., "Buddhism,"* Collier's Encyclopedia, *IV, 176.*

3. *Leslie A. White,* The Science of Culture *(New York: Farrar, Straus and Company, 1949), p. 349n.*

4. *B. F. Skinner, "On Having a Poem,"* Saturday Review, *55 (July 15, 1972), 32-35. He recognizes further that he is "threatening a traditional belief in a creative mind."*

5. *Ibid., p. 34c.*

6. *White,* The Science of Culture, *p. 29.*

7. *In a review of* Verbal Behavior *(The Century Psychology Series), (New York: Appleton-Century-Crofts, Inc., 1957), appearing in* Language, *35 (1959), 26-58.*

8. *In Noam Chomsky, "Language and the Mind I,"* The Columbia University Forum, *Spring 1968, p. 9.*

9. *Ibid. Nevertheless, this does not rule out the fact that for Chomsky, the "postulated mental structures and processes" might be eventually related to some physiological mechanism, or—in his terms—"accounted for in some concrete terms, conceivably, in terms that are not within the range of physical processes as presently understood." That is, in spite of his rejection of the behaviorism of Skinner and his insistence on the creativity of man with language, it is by no means certain that Chomsky rejects, ultimately, a mechanistic view of language or man—a view in which the processes of language would turn out to be completely mechanistic if all the physical facts, internal and external to man, were understood—a fact "which, if correct, should surprise no one" (see p. 10).*

10. *In an article entitled "Language," in* Christ and the Modern Mind, *ed. Robert W. Smith (Downers Grove, Ill.: InterVarsity Press, 1972), pp. 59-68.*

11. *Leonard Bloomfield,* Language *(New York: Henry Holt and Company, 1933).*

12. *Francis A. Schaeffer,* Back to Freedom and Dignity *(Downers Grove, Ill.: InterVarsity Press, 1971), p. 42.*

13. *"Bi-Dialectalism: The Linguistics of White Supremacy,"* English Journal, *58 (Dec. 1969), 1314-15.*

14. *Joseph G. Jorgensen, "On Ethics and Anthropology,"* Current Anthropology, *12 (1971), 321-34; with further material by Richard N. Adams and others.*
15. *See* Newsletter *of the American Anthropological Association, 11, No. 7.*
16. *Ibid., pp. 2, 19-21, 25.*
17. *The poem appears originally in* Mark My Words *(Grand Rapids: Eerdmans, 1971), p. 107. The version given here is taken from* Poetics, *1, No. 1 (1971), 44-45, from an article entitled "Implications of the Patterning of an Oral Reading of a Set of Poems."*
18. *B. F. Skinner,* Beyond Freedom and Dignity *(New York: Bantam Books, Inc., 1972), p. 189.*

Whole People and Half Truths
by Walter R. Hearn

I am a biochemist. My research has been supported largely by the National Institutes of Health, touching on antibiotics, hormones and metabolism, but I have never worked on problems attracting public attention. I try to keep informed on controversial issues in my field, but my knowledge comes secondhand. I have never testified before Congress, been supported by the Department of Defense, served on N.I.H. review panels or otherwise been connected with "big science"—or perhaps even with important science. My areas of research have been so limited that I can speak for "biochemists" with no more assurance than I could speak for "scientists" in general or for "modern man."

So, as one biochemist, and an insignificant one, I want to share with you some ethical questions that have bothered me in my daily work. In comparison to weighty matters discussed at this conference, my own ethical concerns may seem trivial. They are very personal, possibly not felt by other scientists. Or I may be particularly sensitive to them because of my personal biochemistry or my Christian commitment. The fact is that I became a Christian before I became a scientist. Christianity would in that sense have a prior claim on my life even if religious questions were not more basic than scientific questions. I have tried to "bear true faith and allegiance" to science, but with a certain reservation. I felt the same reservation when I took the oath of induction into the military in World War II. I was not sure then that as a Christian I could honestly swear to carry out any order given me. I wondered if the day would come when my prior commitment to Jesus Christ would put me in conflict with military authority.

When I entered a scientific career, I again wondered if conflicts might lie ahead. It turned out that neither in the military nor in science did I have to compromise my Christian convictions. In the service I played an insignificant stateside role, managing with God's help even to make peace in a few lives. Likewise, whatever the role of science in intensifying warfare or in opening a Pandora's box of biological evil, my role in these adventures has been insignificant. So if this country's military or its science has done evil, my contribution to both has been more as a taxpayer than as a direct participant. As a citizen of a democracy, of course, I must recognize and accept my share of any collective guilt.

DAY-TO-DAY ETHICAL PROBLEMS

The question here, though, is not so much what biochemistry may do to the world, but what biochemistry may be doing to me. The *practice* of science is of more immediate concern to me than the *results* of scientific work. Overwhelming ethical problems have a certain attraction for all of us: When guilt is widespread, at least it can be shared. When we focus on ethical dimensions of our own circumstances, if guilt is revealed it is likely to be our own. But before we make judgments about major or public ethical problems, we should honestly face our day-to-day private ethical problems.

We generally have to face such problems alone. Our private circumstances are unique. Who could help us? Confidences should not be broken, and even to question some things openly is to "rock the boat." But the ideal of Christian brotherhood is a spirit of openness, humility, encouragement and exhortation. To share our workaday problems in this spirit must surely be valuable.

There has always been a modest amount of helpful discussion

about the influence of Christian commitment on one's daily work. When I was a young Christian, it seemed to center on the question of what a bartender should do if he were converted to Christ. In our church covenant we had agreed not to use or sell alcoholic beverages; in our community at that time it was illegal to sell liquor-by-the-drink; and I assume that others in the discussion, like myself, had never seen a bar, let alone been inside one. I understood from reading on the subject that some people with no minister of God to turn to when troubled often unburdened themselves to friendly bartenders. I still do not know if that is true, but on the basis of it I argued that a Christian bartender might have an unusually effective ministry. I was always outnumbered in those arguments.

Last year I noticed on my federal income tax return that one could deduct a bribe, provided it was not paid to a government official. I thought that odd until a few weeks later, when my eyes were opened by a book on the new-book shelf in the university library. It was called *The Meat Handbook,* written for buyers and users of meat in commercial restaurants. I was impressed by the candor of the book because of an entire chapter entitled "Commercial Bribery." Evidently nefarious practices are so much a part of the wholesale meat trade, and perhaps of other trades as well, that the government recognizes that one may be forced to give or take bribes as a part of one's professional life. Looking at broad-scale abuses of economic, political and military power today, one may well ask what a restaurant owner or a physician or a congressman or a young person facing the draft should do if he became a Christian. It is easy for someone who has never been in a bar to say that the converted bartender should seek other employment. It is easy to say that a meat buyer should stop paying bribes to get good cuts of meat, even if it means his restaurant has to close. But what shall we say of ourselves?

I am not arguing here whether or not a Christian can be a bartender—or a biochemist. I am saying that if a Christian is a scientist, he will face ethical problems directly associated with his professional life. This will be true even if he is not in "big science" or weapons research or investigations on human subjects or in work which may lead more or less directly to the cloning of human beings.

I will consider three arenas of ethical decision that characterize a scientist's profession: the justification, publication and mechanization of scientific work.

JUSTIFICATION OF SCIENTIFIC WORK

Scientific work can be justified on either of two grounds. Science can help solve technological problems; that is, it is potentially useful. Science also expands our intellectual horizons, whether or not it is useful; that is, it is intrinsically interesting. The relative importance of these grounds has been debated over the years, and styles change from time to time. A few years ago I asked a seminar of new graduate students on which basis they tended to justify their participation in science. All but one said it was the intellectual activity in itself that attracted them. Two years later, when I asked the entering class the same question, all but one said they primarily wanted to do something useful.

People in many walks of life feel no need to justify their work in philosophical terms. A person needs a living and if his work offers "a good living" that is justification enough. I was brought up to think of the expansion of knowledge as a good in itself, and happily discovered that the pursuit of scientific knowledge was not only enjoyable but also profitable. It was easy in the days of my youth to make "a good living" in science without cut-throat competition. It never seemed unfair to me that academic salaries should be lower than the incomes of, say, appliance salesmen, since research was so much more rewarding to the mind and spirit. To get me to sell refrigerators or work in a factory, you would have to pay me a lot; to get me to do scientific work, all you would have to do is provide a laboratory.

But there is the rub. Laboratories are expensive. A young

biochemist is provided with lab benches, the necessary plumbing, the glassware and chemicals left by the former occupants, access to some of his colleagues' equipment and encouragement to scrounge for research funds wherever he can find them. Essentially all biochemical work is done on grants obtained by the investigator himself. There is no other way to obtain the equipment, supplies and technical assistance necessary to do the job. Hence every few years, sometimes every year, one has to justify his work in considerable detail to granting agencies.

I find this procedure fraught with ethical decisions. Suppose I have a really good idea that I am reasonably sure no one else has had, and I know I can learn something interesting from exploring it. Yet it will cost many thousands of dollars to answer the question I have posed. I can even see how the answer might contribute to the solution of some practical problem. At least it will probably not do anyone any harm.

With my naturally optimistic spirit and good imagination, it is hardly a breach of my ethical standards to "slant" my request to a particular granting agency. I can imagine how my work might be potentially useful, so I expand on this theme for the application. After all, mission-oriented agencies understand that Congress has left the support of basic research largely up to them. If my idea is good and I can supply a page or even a paragraph telling how it might someday, somehow, lead to a cure for some disease, any disease, that is enough—at least when research budgets are increasing. Lately, though, it has not been enough, even for mature investigators. Making my pure research project sound like an attempt to solve a practical problem has never seemed dishonest to me, if the granting agency really wants to support basic research and requires only a minimal statement of practical justification.

My problem is that my imagination does not stop there. I can imagine that many other biochemists have thought up equally interesting projects and are equally good at suggesting practical applications. I suspect they may be as worthy of support as I am. I tell myself that this competitive system is good for all of us. It forces each to do his best, to come up with the best possible proposal. It gives us access to critical judgment by competent specialists, a valuable form of continuing education in what is acceptable to the scientific community. It is basically a good system, I tell myself while preparing my application, and I convince myself that I should feel that way even if I lose. Somebody has to lose, I tell myself, or the system would not work so well.

But the fact is that I do not want to lose, and I know that none of the other applicants wants to lose either. None of us can afford to lose, because our careers depend almost entirely on the grant support we bring to our institutions by this process. If we win, we win the opportunity to continue proving our worth. If we lose, or if we lose many times, we have lost everything. The system is good—for the winners. It may even be good for the losers, to weed them out before they invest too much of themselves in this kind of competition.

But there is great temptation when one is in a competition he cannot afford to lose. I have often debated with myself over grant budgets: Will my request for that piece of equipment make it look padded? Better leave it out; maybe a modest request will stand a better chance if the agency's budget is tight. Then I kick myself after the grant is awarded: Why didn't I leave it in? I should have known my idea was good enough to win, and that was a necessary piece of equipment. Don't granting agencies want to help you modernize your laboratory? But is any piece of equipment absolutely necessary?

I have also grappled with the choice of an exciting but risky proposal versus a dull but safe one. For the next grant, I must have publications from this one, to show that I am worth investing in. So it is wise to include more than one idea, with at least one that is bound to pay off. It is tempting, in fact, to propose work already done but still unpublished. That would guarantee a satisfactory return on the grantor's investment in you, setting you up for the next application. And so on, never lying, but shaping the truth to make sure you do not lose.

It is clear that the competition is becoming more intense, since the number of scientists depending on grant funds has grown more rapidly than the funds. Also, the neglected needs of the country for things other than scientific research have become so obvious that it is hard to be enthusiastic even about winning. What right have I to use public money to do what I enjoy when human misery could be alleviated with that money? My own conscience has been assuaged by the fact that I have not used public money to build up a scientific empire. Almost all of the grant money I personally have received has been used for graduate student stipends or for technicians who relieve my students of routine work.

Now, my conscience is not clear even about that. My Ph.D. and M.S. candidates have all found useful work in science so far, but how long can that go on? Where will *their* research money come from? And what if I have trained them to enjoy repeating the process, training more graduate students, who in their turn will train more, and so on? Resources are limited on our planet, and who has the right to do more than reproduce himself? Is it really society's needs that demand the training of more scientists in our image—or is it the demands of our own egos?

There remains the possibility of actually devoting oneself to solving a specific problem facing society today. Some of my colleagues seem to be taking this course, some out of genuinely altruistic motives, others for self-preservation. As I see the major human problems, however, any contributions from my discipline will be relatively insignificant. The real needs are in the realms of personal and social motivation, of economics and of political justice. Each person must do what he can. Maybe one thing he can do is to quit and take up entirely different work. But a person needs a living. . . . By this time biochemistry is beginning to look like selling refrigerators. It *is* a good living, and people need refrigerators, don't they?

PUBLICATION OF SCIENTIFIC WORK
I tend to regard the students I have trained as my primary

contribution; most others regard their published papers as theirs. I know, however, that whatever my students and I may accomplish, it is really our publications that constitute our contribution to science itself. If I have put most of my effort into training students rather than into publishing papers, in the last analysis I was training them to do publishable work and so to publish their own papers. Whether they work for practical or philosophical ends, the truth that comes from their seeking will be deposited in "the literature" to be used by others.

The scientific literature is vast and heterogeneous, but in general is a reliable body of objective truth. The publication system is set up to insure this, with editors and referees intent on eliminating ambiguous descriptions, unjustified conclusions or any subjective elements such as personal bias or esoteric style. Our literature is not revered by scientists, as the Scriptures are by Christians, but it is highly respected. It is ultimately where we make our contribution, and gain our reputation.

"Publish or perish" concisely and more or less accurately states the conditions under which scientific work is done. It is a good system, I think, but there are some problems built into it. More and more scientists, in a more and more competitive atmosphere, will publish more and more papers. Even if the quality of publication is maintained, the relative incremental value of each paper becomes less and less. There seems little doubt that increasing competition does push people into multiplying their bibliographies for reasons of self-preservation. Grants, promotions, employment—everything depends on one's bibliography.

Public problems engendered by the exponentially growing scientific literature have been discussed repeatedly in recent years: how to finance it, search it, store it, and maintain its quality and usefulness. The personal problems of publication are the ones I would like to touch on briefly here. In twenty years of scientific work I have published, on the average, one technical paper a year—enough to keep from perishing if not from languishing somewhat. The ethical crunch I have felt is similar to what I have said about applying for research funds. Scientific publication is supposed to be for the benefit of others, but, if one's life depends on it, it is hard to sort out one's motives. There is the temptation to try to make myself look good. If I am tempted, it is likely that others are tempted. If I am in competition with them for a place in the journals, how do I behave?

Outright fraud must be extremely rare in scientific publication. Who can cite more than one or two instances he knows or suspects in all the literature in his field? In my experience with writing, editing and refereeing papers, the ethical questions have been much more subtle than that. For example, when should we publish? When we are reasonably sure, but still might be mistaken? Wouldn't it be better to wait until we have the whole problem solved unequivocally? But what if we wait and get scooped? Then we might not be able to publish at all. I could stand to miss out on one more paper, but if my student does not have a publication from his thesis will he be able to get a good research job? I suppose I have erred both ways, sometimes publishing too soon, more often not publishing soon enough. In light of the "publication explosion," one might think of withholding publication as a virtue. Not to my former student whose dissertation remains unpublished!

In putting together a scientific paper, the finest nuances of wording can have ethical implications. Experiments that have been done for a variety of reasons, some of them foolish, can be strung together in a sequence that shows a logical progression of thought. The data are presented faithfully, but the author comes out as the clever person he would like to have been at the time he did the experiments. Eventually comes the temptation to make oneself look good even at the expense of others. In a paper in press this year I wanted to show what a useful analytical technique we had developed. If our method had been available to him, it would have kept another investigator from drawing an erroneous conclusion in an earlier paper. In the first draft of our paper I wrote that his conclusion was "erroneous."

In a later draft I softened that word to "unwarranted." Finally, my co-author on the paper said, "Look, that fellow is a friend of mine. I don't want to put him down, even if he made a mistake." So the paper as published now says that his conclusion, based on insufficient evidence, was "premature."

That is a small thing, and it is part of the scientific process to show that your method, your conclusion, your theory, is superior to what has gone before. You know that your own work will be improved upon and perhaps forgotten. There should be no hard feelings about that. "When the perfect comes, the imperfect will pass away." If we are devoted to the search for truth, we should be glad to see our work proved in error or our conclusions revealed as premature. But who is up to that? The temptation is to make ourselves look as mature, correct, wise, clever, as anyone else in the game—in fact, to make ourselves look better than our competitors. Would we do that if they were all our *friends*? Has the system put us at enmity with those who should be colleagues in the joyous pursuit of truth?

I have sometimes argued with other Christians on behalf of the objective, impersonal character of scientific publication. I think it is good that my scientific papers do not reveal or even hint that I am a Christian. There are other places for that. The scientific literature would be far less reliable, far more removed from truth, if our biases and feelings could be expressed in it. But even with the limitations imposed, the truth is distorted, if ever so slightly, by our personal stake in it. I feel this most keenly perhaps when I am called on to referee someone else's manuscript for a scientific journal. There are stories of unethical practices by referees, using privy information for their own benefit. I have been delivered from such gross temptation. But suppose the rejection rate of the journal is high. It is fifty per cent for some journals. I know the editor expects me to be critical. If the paper is not up to my standards, it is my responsibility to slash it or recommend rejection. That is beneficial to science as a whole and educational for the author. But I also know how I feel when a referee has been harsh on a manuscript of mine. Who is not influenced by the treatment his own papers have received? And who has not felt elated by a really weak paper on which to exercise judgment? Who can tell when his personal feelings get in the way of his objective reasoning? Who is not tempted to denounce the speck in his brother's manuscript in spite of, or because of, the log in his own?

MECHANIZATION OF SCIENTIFIC WORK

Many of us were attracted to science in the first place by its promise to simplify the phenomena of the universe. Even in the biological sciences with their unending variety we see progress along these lines: Laws and paradigms begin to bring satisfying clarity out of complexity. But, at the same time, the tools with which we arrive at these generalizations become ever more complex. To simplify nature we must complicate the process of studying nature. However human our desire to understand the world, we find we must depend more and more on instruments, computers, machines, to do it. It is as though we cannot know God's world in detail without replacing it with a world of our own making.

I suppose that many things simply cannot be done without reliance on machines, including science. But it bothers me to see myself becoming so dependent that the machine begins to control the course of my investigation. For example, I once found it necessary to have an expensive piece of equipment to solve a particular analytical problem. No such instrument was available at my university. I could give up and change the direction of my investigation; I could move permanently or temporarily to another laboratory where an instrument was available; or my students and I could do the analyses laboriously by hand. But graduate students' research depended on the analyses and I could not ask them to spend that much time on routine work. If we wanted the work done, I had either to obtain the analytical instrument or hire a technician. Economics dictated the purchase of the instrument, even though ultimately that meant hiring an analyst to feed the machine anyway. For the same investment in technical help, we could do far more work if we had the instrument.

An offer of a job at another institution gave me some leverage at the time, so I was able to persuade the dean to provide half the funds for the instrument. The other half was squeezed from my grant, of course. I was now free to solve the problem in the best possible way, in fact in almost the only way it could be solved. But, alas, it then became necessary to choose problems which had to be solved with the aid of the instrument in order to justify its purchase and the salary of the technician to run it. If the machine and the technician were not both kept busy, we were wasting the taxpayers' money. Besides, if not used, both would get so out of condition that results would be questionable when we did need to count on the instrument to solve a problem. So to feed the machine I had to build up an empire I did not want, or I had to hustle samples from other laboratories, in the process becoming a manager instead of a scientist.

"Did that which is good, then, bring death to me?" I am afraid it did. But perhaps in one sense it brought life also. After the instrument was delivered, I spent a week at the manufacturer's training course for operators of the instrument, with perhaps thirty other people from around the country. Something about that week got to me. The instrument at that time cost about $14,000. Inflation and increased sophistication have pushed the price up to $18,000 or $20,000 by now. It occurred to me that each of the thirty people in the class was of infinitely more worth than that, but we had not come together to learn how to draw the best out of each other. We were there to focus on this machine because it was worth $14,000 and we were obligated to treat it well and maximize its great potential.

I tried to get to know some of my classmates, but it was difficult. They were intent on their responsibility to master the instrument, and at the end of each day they rushed to anesthetize themselves at the free bar provided by the manufacturer. They could stand the company of the machine without the palliative effect of alcohol, but not the company of other human beings. That made me sad, but it gave me time alone to think about what I valued most, both as a creature of God and as a scientist. Was I really doing science for humane reasons, either to be of service to other people through my discoveries or to expand my own human potential? Or had I chained myself to a machine, not just this instrument but the whole mechanical enterprise, the scientific establishment, whether or not it was good for people or for me as a person?

In science, as in other fields, the machines we have increasingly come to rely on are highly complex, "almost human." But as machines take on more human attributes, we see human beings not freed to become more human, as we had hoped, but constrained to become more and more like machines. This mechanization of people seems to come not so much from understanding ourselves mechanistically as from competing among ourselves for the available resources. Machines perform subhuman tasks more efficiently than humans can. One makes a machine of himself simply by limiting himself to a single objective at a time. That is the way to "get things done." Competition forces us to that kind of efficiency. In the course of a scientific career we may have to drop other aspects of life to become first a grade-grinding machine, then a data-collecting machine, a computing machine, a grant-getting machine, a teaching machine and finally a machine-tending machine. Scientific work is intense and competitive. And although it is a human enterprise, it is not necessarily a humane one.

We are whole people when we start out to do scientific work, whole people seeking the whole truth. In our role as scientists we learn to settle for less than the whole truth. But to gain even the half-truths that our work can produce, we see ourselves having to sacrifice something of our wholeness. To continue to do good scientific work it may be necessary to ignore or suppress this understanding. We must get on with the work and not think about what we are doing to ourselves and to the next generation of young scientists we are training.

To some of us, this may be the most painful ethical dilemma of all. If we remain as whole people, we see that we are dealing with half-truths. But the whole truth may contain the knowledge that we are making half-people of ourselves. What shall we do? Is everyone in the same situation? Is there anything better than science we could do? Or is there a better way to do science?

I do not know. But I want to find out. At present I have taken a year's leave of absence to think about whether I want to go back to scientific work. Science has been a satisfying career for me, the best "Establishment" career I can think of. I have the security of a tenured position; I associate with people of intelligence and integrity; I have far more freedom than the refrigerator salesman; and I work in a park-like campus setting.

But "There Are Men Too Gentle to Live Among Wolves." I suspect that there are men too thoughtful to compete with machines. Or perhaps just too inefficient.

At any rate, I have one more month in which to decide.

III

Ethics in Genetics

Genetic Control
and Human Values
by V. Elving Anderson

Not long ago discussions of genetics were accompanied by a sense of fatalism, as though nothing could be changed. Now the mood has changed to one of apprehension and even fear, as though too much might be changed. This shift in attitude parallels the general public ambivalence toward other areas of science and technology.

Genetic control of man has obvious social, psychological and ethical implications. For this reason responsible scientists have tried to involve citizens in dialogue to explore the issues before new means of control become available and choices become necessary. It is my impression, however, that speculations about future possibilities actually may reduce the ability of society and of individuals to cope with the questions. If fear is a common response, as I suspect, such efforts to anticipate the future may be counterproductive and a re-evaluation of strategy may be helpful.

FIVE GUIDELINES
In this spirit I wish to suggest five guidelines that have helped me to gain some sense of coherence. Then I will discuss selected aspects of genetic control and indicate the human values that appear to be involved.

1. For individuals and families burdened with genetic diseases, the possibilities of control are most welcome. Research in human genetics is motivated by sincere efforts to alleviate suf-

fering as well as by the fundamental search for new knowledge and understanding common to all of science. The fear of genetic control generally is directed toward the possibility of authoritarian coercion rather than toward the methods themselves.

2. A heavy emphasis on the possible threats posed by future developments in genetic technology tends to obscure the important problems encountered at the present time. A resolution of the present issues should have priority in public discussion. Demonstrated ability to cope with the present should make it easier for us to face future questions.

3. Many of the questions involve a conflict between two or more human values. Efforts to simplify issues by failing to recognize such tensions are misleading. Furthermore, in a pluralistic society such as ours individuals will tend to place a different emphasis on the competing values. Such variability makes it essential for us to protect freedom to arrive at different decisions.

4. The claim has been advanced that the issues posed by genetic technology are so unique that "old values" will be completely inadequate. This approach seems to reflect a rejection of the continuity of human history. It also suggests that adequate answers must await a total review of the strategies of valuing. It is not surprising that lay persons respond with a spirit of frustration and fear of the future. Empirically one can review the current and projected technologies for genetic control and can identify the ethical and moral issues. Then we can ask if any fundamentally new questions are involved. My impression is that, when unmasked, the issues will be familiar.

5. When considering topics with important social implications, it is essential to give careful attention to the manner in which questions are framed. The environmental crisis has arisen in part because either narrow questions were posed (dealing only with the immediate effectiveness of specific technologies) or no questions at all, until the damage was done. A rapid development and utilization of genetic control could have even more disastrous consequences if the questions are limited to

techniques for the manipulation of genetic material. It is at this point that views of the nature of man become crucial. Geneticists understandably must view man as *biological organism,* but a parallel concern for man as *responsible self* is also needed.

GENETIC COUNSELING (THE ETHICS OF DECIDING)

Genetic counseling involves the use of genetic information to promote the welfare of individuals, families and society. If the best interests at these three levels appear to conflict, then priorities probably should be considered in that order, protecting first the welfare of individuals.

When parents know that there is a sizable risk of producing another child with a serious defect, they should consider setting aside their privilege of further reproduction in order to protect the right of children to be wellborn. Recent evidence indicates that parents making such decisions place more weight on the *burden* (the effects of the disease on the child, together with the physical, emotional and financial load for the parents) than on the *risk* (the probability that the child will be affected).[1] As a simple example, the risk of repetition within a family is the same for hemophilia and color blindness, but the burden obviously is much greater for hemophilia.

The right to privacy and the need for truth-telling usually would be considered worthy objectives, but they may come into tension in the counseling situation. When a diagnosis of a genetic disorder is made, the physician has a responsibility to explain the nature of the disorder and its treatment. Should the physician also explore the implications for further reproduction, even though this means raising a question that was not asked in the original consultation? By all means, since the physician's concern legitimately extends to the family unit, including those children who might yet be born. It may be more difficult to decide about other relatives, who may be at risk for the condition but whose privacy must be invaded to tell them the "truth" about which they did not ask and which they may prefer not to hear. And what should be done if no help can be offered to the relatives, such as when they are not likely to have more children or when no treatment for the disorder is available?

To what extent should the values of the genetic counselor enter into the discussion and the decision making process? It is generally assumed that the freedom of the individual should be respected and protected, but choices can be modified by the manner in which information is presented. Garret Hardin has claimed, for example, that "the counselor may, to secure acceptance of the truth, pretend to leave the decision up to the client, but this pretense is only tactical. The responsibility for really making the decision must rest on the shoulders of the professional."[2] This extreme view probably would not be accepted by most workers in this area, but it states the issue clearly. One measure that has been proposed for the "effectiveness" of genetic counseling is the extent to which subsequent reproduction in the family was curtailed, but this implies that "good" counseling should affect reproduction markedly. On the other hand, some individuals or families may be overwhelmed by the apparent complexity of the situation in which they find themselves and may need assistance.

POPULATION SCREENING (THE ETHICS OF KNOWING)
Genetic counseling usually involves families in which a problem already is known. For some conditions it has recently become possible to screen a general population, without knowing in advance which individuals may be affected.

Two types of screening situations can be described: First, individuals *affected* with certain specific disorders may be detected before any clinical problem is observed and early enough to permit some intervention to reduce the effects of the disease. Phenylketonuria (PKU), for example, is one of the genetic causes of mental retardation. Affected children lack an enzyme needed for the body to use one of the common amino acids in food. The condition can be detected three to five days after birth by analysis of a few drops of blood obtained by a heel prick. Careful diagnosis must follow in order to eliminate "false positives." Then a special diet, low in the particular amino acid, can be used.

Second, for some conditions it is possible to detect *carriers* of a gene who will not be affected themselves but who can pass the gene on to their children. If both husband and wife are carriers of the same gene, there is a twenty-five percent chance for each child to get both genes and develop the problem. Here the best illustrations would be sickle cell anemia (relatively common in blacks and in some persons of Mediterranean origin) and Tay-Sachs disease (a cause of blindness, paralysis and death which is most common in Ashkenazi Jews).

What are the requirements for such screening tests? They must be simple and inexpensive so that large numbers of individuals can be tested. The testing procedure must not be harmful in itself. The end results must be accurate, since either over-diagnosis or under-diagnosis could be very misleading. Finally, the conclusions must be interpreted adequately to the persons involved so that they understand the implications. This may appear simple, but a number of medical, legal, psychological and sociological issues have arisen in trying to apply such tests.

In the case of PKU most states in this country passed screening laws in the years 1963 to 1967. In a wave of enthusiasm some of the laws went too far in specifying the method of diagnosis and even of treatment.[3] Since medical knowledge may change rapidly it is obviously unwise to build current knowledge into law. In some parts of the country adequate diagnostic tests to verify the screening results were not readily available, and misdiagnosis led to attempted treatment which was harmful and apparently killed some children. In addition, the new screening procedures identified milder cases of PKU that had been missed before, and it was not at all clear that the usual treatment by special diet was desirable. A main lesson is that a desire for rapid use of new medical knowledge in the delivery of health care must be tempered with caution and wide consultation.

Another set of problems has arisen concerning screening for sickle cell gene carriers. The basic difficulty lies in a genetic change in the hemoglobin molecule so that the molecules stack up in rods and distort the red blood cell. Those who have a double dose of the gene develop a severe *anemia*. Those with only a single dose, however, are described as having the sickle cell *trait* and have little if any medical problems as carriers.

Among U.S. blacks roughly 1/400 has the anemia, while one out of ten is a carrier with the trait. If a mother is a carrier and the status of the father is unknown, the risk for a child to get two genes and develop anemia is 1/40. On the other hand, if both mother and father are known to be carriers, the risk of anemia for a child is 1/4. Accurate and relatively simple tests for the carrier status are available, and recently there have been massive efforts to carry out screening of large populations.

Since blacks are primarily involved, the possibilities of racist overtones are obvious. Two types of reactions from black communities have been reported: Why did you wait so long to pay attention to this problem which is so important to blacks? Why is "Whitey" so interested now? (Isn't this merely another effort at genocide?)

Perhaps more fundamental is the question of freedom versus coercion. Massachusetts passed a law in 1971 "requiring the testing of blood for sickle trait or anemia as a prerequisite for school attendance." For persons with the anemia, the knowledge of the reasons for their condition (if not known already) may help in getting adequate treatment. For the carrier, there are three main options for marriage and reproduction: (1) Choose a noncarrier as a mate, (2) if married to a carrier, plan not to reproduce, or (3) if children are born, have them checked for the possibility of anemia.

Although there still may be areas of disagreement, some general principles have emerged for screening procedures like those for sickle cell. First, screening should be voluntary. Such a procedure may be less efficient in reaching large populations, and better educational efforts will be required, but the program will be better accepted and understood. Programs for diabetes testing or chest X-rays might provide a basis for experience. Second, screening without counseling is worse than no screening at all. Incomplete or inaccurate information can have a devastating effect upon one's self-image. Third, the *right of privacy* for the results of the screening should be maintained.[4]

PRENATAL DIAGNOSIS AND SELECTIVE ABORTION (FREEDOM AND RESPONSIBILITY)

Within the past few years it has become possible to diagnose certain genetic conditions in a fetus. There had been a standard procedure for withdrawing some of the fluid surrounding the developing fetus (a process known as amniocentesis) in order to monitor the status of the pregnancy, but then it was realized that fetal cells from the amniotic fluid could be used to detect the sex of the fetus, chromosome anomalies (such as mongolism) and enzyme deficiencies.

Amniocentesis is usually delayed until a time when enough amniotic fluid has accumulated to reduce the possibility of harm to the fetus, after about thirteen weeks of pregnancy. Although some tests can be carried out as soon as the fluid is removed, accurate diagnosis requires growth of the cells in tissue culture, which may take two or three weeks. On occasion the cells fail to grow, but when tissue growth occurs the diagnosis is essentially one-hundred per cent accurate.

These points may be illustrated with reference to Tay-Sachs disease, a condition most commonly found among Ashkenazi Jews and only rarely in other groups. There is a deficiency in an enzyme which is needed to break down lipid materials which otherwise accumulate in nerve and other cells. The results of this accumulation are progressive blindness and paralysis, and usually death by age two years. If one child is affected, both parents are carriers and there is a twenty-five per cent risk for each subsequent pregnancy.

Now that an accurate test for enzyme levels in fetal cells has been developed, prenatal diagnosis can be requested in an additional pregnancy. In fact, it may become accepted medical practice to expect the physician to notify such a couple that prenatal diagnosis is possible. This does not mean that the couple would be required to have such a test, but they must decide either to "take their chances" or "find out the facts."

Discussions about abortion often assume that the only issue is the sanctity of life or that the only issue is individual freedom. This is unfortunate since both principles are involved and both have a biblical basis. Some further consideration of their relationship to prenatal diagnosis may help us understand our own values.

This situation is not an "unwanted" pregnancy in the sense of a selfish emotional rejection of an unfortunate child. A reluctance to terminate a pregnancy is counterbalanced by a deep concern for the welfare of a child who would be doomed to a short life of illness and then death. We are dealing here with the "right to be born," but we should consider whether such a right means mere existence or whether it includes some concern for the quality of existence.

Parents make other sorts of choices on behalf of their children. Does parental responsibility extend to a decision that a specific child should not be born at all? The concepts of God as Creator and man as steward anticipate man's power to control, but do not indicate the course of action in this most difficult circumstance. If a choice is to be made, I would argue that it should be the responsibility of the parents rather than some external group (medical or legal). They may need help and counsel, however, in facing the emotional consequences.

The Bible does not give us much direct help on this point. The only record of miscarriage is in Exodus 21, shortly after the presentation of the Ten Commandments. An injury to a pregnant woman leading to miscarriage took place under circumstances that do not appear relevant to the present problem. Other portions of the Bible relate to the more general questions, however, and it may not be wise to pursue too strongly an argument from silence.

A symposium sponsored by the Christian Medical Society and *Christianity Today* produced "A Protestant Affirmation on the Control of Human Reproduction."[5] On the topic of abortion the group concluded:

1) The human fetus is not merely a mass of cells or an organic growth. At the most, it is an actual human life or at the least, a potential and developing human life. For this reason the physician with a regard for the value and sacredness of human life will exercise great caution in advising an abortion.

2) The Christian physician will advise induced abortion only to safeguard greater values sanctioned by Scripture. These values should include individual health, family welfare, and social responsibility.

3) From the moment of birth, the infant is a human being with all the rights which Scripture accords to all human beings; therefore, infanticide under any circumstances must be condemned.

What is the status of laws concerning the rights of the fetus? There is clear precedent establishing liability in the case of prenatal injuries and permitting action for "wrongful death" that might result. More recently a principle of "wrongful life" is emerging.[6] In a suit brought on behalf of an illegitimate child, a court agreed that a legal wrong had been committed, but refused to grant relief on the grounds that such recognition would encourage similar action by others "born into the world under conditions they might regard as adverse." More relevant to the genetic situation is a case in which suit was brought on behalf of a congenitally defective child who was born after the mother had German measles during pregnancy and her request for abortion was refused.[7]

Would not relaxed abortion laws encourage a general disregard for human life? Hitler put into effect very rigid laws against abortion, thus providing evidence that antiabortion laws are not necessarily correlated with respect for life. His approach followed from a national population policy at a time of dwindling population and the need for a larger work force. A more general question, then, is the extent to which government should be involved at all in the control of human reproduction.

Returning to the question of prenatal diagnosis, it should be remembered that a family is not forced to make this choice. With something as severe as Tay-Sachs disease, a very satisfactory alternative is to seek permanent contraception by sterilizing either husband or wife. No affected child will be produced. There will be no need for prenatal diagnosis or termination. There will not even be a child carrying the gene, thus helping to reduce the gene frequency (although with only a slight effect).

My own present view on this topic can be summarized as follows:

1. Laws should permit the termination of pregnancy on the basis of the health of the fetus.

2. On the other hand, there should be no laws or regulations which directly or indirectly require or force termination of pregnancy based on the results of prenatal diagnosis.

3. The choice of a couple should not be prejudged. Information about the options open to them should not be withheld on the assumption that they would not or should not be interested.

4. Once a couple has made a decision, their choice should be respected on the basis of their own responsibility before God.

DONOR INSEMINATION

Artificial insemination using the husband's sperm can increase the probability of conception under certain circumstances. More recently frozen sperm storage has been encouraged prior to vasectomy in order to provide the option of additional pregnancies if desired.

Artificial insemination using donor sperm permits what has been called "semi-adoption" when the husband is infertile or is known to carry a harmful gene. A more extensive use of donor sperm banks has been proposed as a means of improving the gene pool.[8]

There are no generally accepted regulations or principles which govern the provision of sperm (fresh or frozen). Although some of the questions are technical, there are ethical issues as well. Here is an area in which "consumer protection" is needed (if that is the appropriate term). Most physicians providing this service no doubt proceed responsibly, but it may be difficult for the prospective recipient to check on matters like the following:

1. There should be guidelines for sperm quality in terms of viability. From the limited experience to date there is no evidence that the freezing of sperm will cause damage to the fetus, but continuing studies are essential. It is more likely that the conditions of freezing may kill some sperm and thus lower the probability of conception. Standards for sperm viability should be established.

2. There should be some limit to the number of conceptions per donor. Unsubstantiated rumors claim that one donor fathered over four hundred children, and such a large number seems unjustified on any grounds. If such a multiple use of donors were frequent, there could be instances of inbreeding in the next generation without knowledge by the parties involved. More serious is the chance of widespread propagation of harmful genes that the donor might be carrying.

3. Adequate genetic data should be maintained for the donor and for the offspring. A family history interview with the donor would provide the basis for an initial screening for conditions having a known genetic basis. If any child produced by insemination turned out to show a genetic problem, the possibility of no longer using sperm from that donor should be considered. There would need to be elaborate precautions in order to preserve privacy.

4. Efforts should be made to reduce the effects of commercialization. For example, in order to prevent conflict of interest, no one associated with a sperm bank should be used as a donor.

SELECTION FOR COMPLEX TRAITS
The most common traits in man turn out to involve a number

of genetic factors as well as an interaction with the environment. For them it is much more difficult to specify the individual genes and outline a program for genetic control, even if this were thought desirable.

There is a legitimate need for public concern lest medical advances and changes in social policy modify differential reproduction and lead to an increase in disorders such as diabetes. Unfortunately, we do not know enough yet about the genetic basis for diabetes to make a reasonable estimate of what will happen to its frequency in the future. Treatment of diabetics does improve their reproductive potential and may lead to an increase in genetic predisposition for future generations, but the rate of change probably will be considerably less than popular fears suggest.

Similar concern has been expressed about the genetic basis for intelligence, as measured by IQ tests. On the average, less able children tend to come from larger families, and this observation has led to the fear of a general decline in the genetic basis for intellectual potential. Such observations, however, fail to take into account those retarded people who have not had children at all. When a proper comparison is made between one generation and the next there is no evidence for a net change in the frequency of genes underlying the IQ distribution.

A more controversial point has been introduced by the speculations of Dr. William Shockley. He assumes that the IQ differences between black and white groups have a genetic basis and has urged more careful studies. Meanwhile as a remedy he has proposed that individuals be offered a bonus for voluntary sterilization—a sum of one thousand dollars for each IQ point under 100. In my opinion, this suggestion reflects a gross misunderstanding of the genetic issues involved and a cruel social insensitivity.

Although there is much left for us to learn, the following points can be made: (1) There is good evidence that a significant proportion of variation in IQ scores within groups can be attributed to genetic factors. (2) Current estimates of heritability *within* groups for IQ are inflated, however, mainly because of the great difficulty in identifying significant environmental variables and genotype-environment interactions. (3) The heritability of IQ differences *between* racial or ethnic groups cannot be estimated (even crudely) at the present. It is the difficulty of the problem, not merely fear, that makes progress in research slow. (4) Even if heritability could be estimated adequately, the meaning of such estimates for human behavior is more limited than is sometimes claimed. (5) There is indeed the need for further research, but the questions should be put into a form such that the answers will be perceived as helpful to the persons involved, and not threatening or harmful.

Topics such as this present important ethical problems both to the research worker and to the humanitarian. A statement by Victor Weisskopf has helped to resolve the tension: "Science cannot develop unless it is pursued for the sake of pure knowledge and insight. But it will not survive unless it is used intensely and wisely for the betterment of humanity, and not as an instrument of domination by one group over another. There are two powerful elements in human existence: compassion and curiosity. Curiosity without compassion is inhuman; compassion without curiosity is ineffective."[9] This type of balance parallels Paul's admonition about "speaking the truth in love."[10]

CLONING

One of the most controversial and speculative topics about genetic control is that of cloning. Basically this term means asexual reproduction, but current discussions include two separate ideas.

One idea is that from the genetic point of view the most significant feature of sexual reproduction is recombination of the genetic material. The theoretical number of different combinations of chromosomes that could be produced in the formation of eggs (or sperm) by one individual is at least 2^{23}. The only assurance that a couple can have for their next child is that it will be different from their previous ones. The possibility of a harmful new combination would be prevented if we could start with a combination already known to be a good one. The technique generally proposed would be to remove the nucleus from a fertilized ovum (by microsurgery or laser beam) and replace it with the nucleus from an adult cell.

A second phase would be to produce a number of humans with the same genetic constitution. This might be done (so the speculation goes) by repeating the process above, inserting nuclei from the same donor into a number of different ova or by separating the cells in an early embryo with the hope that each would develop into a separate human being. To stir the imagination a writer may ask what it would be like to have one hundred Mozarts.

Popular presentations of cloning range from serious efforts at improving the public understanding of science to speculative nonsense. The topic sounds enough like science fiction that it is tempting to exaggerate and mislead. Predictably the responses vary from fascination to utter rejection. More sober reflection suggests that some serious and more fundamental objections can be raised.

1. Enthusiasm for the idea is based on a serious overclaim about the current state of the technology. The proposals are based on nuclear transplants involving frog eggs, but the successful transplants have used nuclei from embryos, or from adults infected with a kidney tumor virus, neither of which is a good model for the human situation. The human ovum is much smaller, although the technical problems probably could be overcome. What is needed is a nucleus that is sufficiently undifferentiated to guide embryonic development, and it is not yet certain that a normal adult nucleus will work—for frog or man. Thus it would seem clear that discussion of cloning in man is premature at best. The details should be worked out first for some domestic animal for which asexual propagation might be advantageous. Only then would it be reasonable to consider the technical aspects of application to man.

2. Cloning does not appear to meet any real human need that cannot be met in some other way. Some of the reasons sound like mere curiosity, to find out "what would happen" if there were indeed one hundred Mozarts. A desire to propagate one's own genetic constitution would be another questionable motivation.

3. Restrictive choices would be made on behalf of the next generation. Some person or committee would have to choose the donor from whom the nucleus would be taken. An unhappy person at present might on occasion choose to "curse God" for his existence. Would it really be any better if there were an individual or group to hold responsible?

4. Important reproductive decisions would be shifted from the family to laboratories. The impression is becoming widespread that advances in reproductive technology have made the family obsolete. We should be reminded that the environmental crisis resulted in part from narrow questions based only on a specific technology. Leon Kass has insisted that "the elimination of the family would weaken ties to past and future, and would throw us, even more than we are now, to the mercy of an impersonal, lonely present."[11]

CONCLUSION

In this brief presentation I have not had the time to deal exhaustively with the human values that are involved in the use of techniques for genetic control. Nevertheless, some of the issues have been identified in the hope of stimulating further discussion and evaluation.

Means to alleviate genetic defects are most welcome to individuals and families that face such problems. Yet the process of making such help available has led to unexpected tensions and misunderstanding. For the most part, the human values are quite recognizable and familiar, even if seen in a new context. For this reason biblical concepts still are quite relevant and helpful.

In an important sense, the consideration of genetic control

forces us to examine our view of human nature, particularly along these lines:

Wholeness. We should view man as both biological organism and responsible self, as Ian Barbour has suggested.[12] Genetic techniques are directed toward man as organism, but the decisions affect personal relationships. A biblical view of man does not stress human frailty so much as distorted personal relationships and responses toward God, and these are part of the total context of genetic control.

Responsibility. Just as we are stewards of God's other good gifts, we are also stewards of the human gene pool.

Freedom. Authoritarian uses of genetic control should be discouraged whenever they seriously restrict human freedoms. Furthermore, choices made by others for themselves should be respected, even if we would disagree.

Family. Reproductive problems should be handled so as to strengthen the role of the family. Biblical views of the family may be much more significant than we have expected and should not be disregarded.

---

1. *Claire O. Leonard, Gary A. Chase and Barton Childs, "Genetic Counseling: A Consumer's View,"* New England Journal of Medicine, *287 (1972), 433-39.*

2. *Garret Hardin,* Nature and Man's Fate *(New York: Rinehart, 1959).*

3. *See Samuel P. Bessman and Judith P. Swazey, "Phenylketonuria: A Study of Biomedical Legislation," in* Human Aspects of Biomedical Innovation, *ed. E. Mendelsohn, J. P. Swazey and L. Taviss (Cambridge: Harvard University Press, 1971), pp. 49-76.*

4. *Marc Lappe, James M. Gustafson and Richard Roblin, "Ethical and Social Issues in Screening for Genetic Disease,"* New England Journal of Medicine, *286 (1972), 1129-32.*

5. *Walter O. Spitz and Carlyle L. Saylor,* Birth Control and the Christian *(Wheaton, Ill.: Tyndale House, 1969).*

6. *Thomas F. Lambert, Jr., "The Legal Rights of the Fetus," in Ibid., pp. 371-414.*

7. *W. Carey Parker, "Some Legal Aspects of Genetic Counseling,"* Progress in Medical Genetics, *7 (1970), 217-31.*

8. *H. J. Muller, "What Genetic Course Will Men Steer?"* Bulletin of the Atomic Scientists, *March 1968, pp. 6-12.*

9. *Victor Weisskopf, "The Significance of Science,"* Science, *176 (1972), 138-46.*

10. *Ephesians 4:15.*

11. *Leon R. Kass, "The New Biology: What Price Relieving Man's Estate?"* Science, *174 (1971), 779-88.*

12. *Ian Barbour,* Science & Secularity: The Ethics of Technology *(New York: Harper & Row, 1970).*

The Ethics of Genetics
by J. Frank Cassel

T he papers in this volume have examined several important issues which face the scientist as he practices his
science—issues which impinge upon him as a member of
both his species and his society and which he cannot rationally
or reasonably dodge by computer-like objectivity. No scientist
can be truly objective. He operates within his own unique and
personal frame of reference. Only as he recognizes and makes
allowance for his biases, prejudices and limitations can he
approach objectivity.

But I feel that sometimes we as scientists restrict our potential as creative investigators by paying too much attention to
method and too little to insight and intuition. The same climate
which prescribes our objective methods also often isolates us
from personal consideration of some of the ramifications of the
knowledge we are accumulating. Some scientists feel that even
though they are committed Christians they must, when they
enter the laboratory, leave Christ at the door and rely only on
observable data. On the other hand, when I carry out my
studies of avian communities, I believe that I not only count
birds as a Christian, but also as a philosopher, artist and psychologist—and as a responsible, social human being. And although my assessment of the number of birds on my study area
on January 10, 1972, would look no different on paper from
that of any other qualified observer in the same situation, it is a
unique study because of its effect on me.

For several years I have been intrigued by the advances in genetics and have been speaking and writing about some of the implications and possibilities, indicating that in this area lie some keys which are vital to man's continued existence.[1] Professor Anderson has pointed out above that geneticists are probing problems not only of existence but of the very nature and potential of our species. While mulling over these problems again as I prepared this paper, I suddenly realized that I personally have been hiding behind the questions I have been asking—that my rhetorical question to my classes, "Who wants to sit on the committee which determines what constitutes a 'better' man?" has been a personal ruse to escape asking myself the next much more important and basic question, "Frank Cassel, if *you* sat on such a committee, what criteria would *you* look for, what data would *you* require, what principles would *you* espouse in making decisions which determine how any scientific advance may be used for the *good* of man?"

First, of course, I must determine what is *good*. That, as I understand it, is what ethics is all about. I have only recently, as I say, tried to face up to this question personally, so I am not very satisfied with my progress. But let me share some of the ways it has been coming together. Some of my proposals are tentative, some simply rational *ad absurdum*'s with which I seem to be stuck.

BASES FOR MY ETHICS

Good can be variously defined. That "there is none good but God" and that I can "be made good with the goodness of God" puts it simply in its biblical framework.[2] But as a "good" man in God's sight, through his grace in the Lord Jesus Christ, and having his "goodness," what do I think and do as a member of my mundane "God-playing" committee. In workaday life, it seems to me that we determine good on at least four bases.

1. *Biblical Good.* If the Bible categorically states something is good, it is good (for example, "Honor your father and

mother"). If the Bible states something is not good (evil), it is not good ("Thou shalt not kill").[3] Professor Stob has raised some pertinent questions about even this categorical.

2. *Moral Good.* Certainly biblical good is moral good but not all situations are covered by Scripture. For example, nowhere does the Bible directly tell me that I shall be as objective as possible in making my observations of birds and that I should report them straightforwardly and honestly. Certainly one could quote passages that relate to this. But these simply parallel and do not establish the ethics of the scientific community. Many of my unbelieving colleagues are more sensitive to this ethic than I am and defend it more vigorously, simply because, as I have said, I personally question the centrality of objectivity.

3. *Legal Good.* People keep telling me "You can't legislate morals" and I keep answering "What else do you legislate?" On the other hand, a traffic light seems to me to be a "legal" good as distinguished from a "moral" good.

4. *Good Established by Mores.* Whether mores are a valid or true basis for "good" is not the immediate issue. The fact is we do make ethical decisions on the basis of mores. Social sanctions are real and widespread—and often irrational. Years ago a friend of mine went from North Dakota to a college in the South. He still recounts his surprise to find that the college community had no scruples against attending movies but strong sanctions against heterosexual swimming parties, while just the opposite had been true at home. Our evangelical communities have wrestled long with taboos. My guess is we will continue to do so for a long time.

Therefore, in making an ethical decision I must, I think, identify the type of good I am considering. Allowing correct interpretation, I have, in the case of biblical goods, only to ascertain what constitutes "honor" or "kill" in the examples I gave. I cannot *ethically* ignore my mother and father. I cannot *ethically* kill with abandon.

Since honesty has sound scriptural undergirding, I cannot *ethically* "bear false witness" to my investigations. On the other

hand, I dare say that my personal stand on objectivity is rub-
bing some of you the wrong way. Has my questioning the actual
role of objectivity in science raised a moral issue or simply one
of viewpoint? If you consider it a moral issue, then my stand is
unethical and as such has little place in the conversation of
reasonable, ethical scientists. It can be ignored. If not, we can
still be in dialogue about it, and maybe even agree to disagree
about it.

In the case of legal good, as long as the law is not in conflict
with the Bible or morals, I cannot *ethically* advocate illegal
actions. I can, on the other hand, strive to change or alter the
law if I feel there is a better alternative. In states where abortion
is still illegal, to advocate ignoring the law is unethical. To work
for liberalizing the law is not. Note carefully that here my distinction between moral good and legal good may be very important. If the laws of your state have been liberalized beyond your
persuasion of the proper limits, your personal decisions will be
based on morals not on law. Liberalized laws do not necessarily
liberalize morals. But since many fear this relationship will exist
in practice, they oppose liberalizing legislation. My point is that
in making a decision I should clearly recognize its real basis.

I think after experiences many of us have had with taboos,
we tend to be skeptical of ethics based on customs. But can we,
at a point of time, always distinguish accurately between a
moral issue and an issue of custom? TV helped us see the fallacy
of certain taboos against movies or at least the inconsistency of
the practice of some saints as compared with their proclamation. But the issue of pornography and suggestiveness as con-
trasted with purity of mind and body is much greater today
than it was thirty years ago. I personally am happy for more
open discussions of sexual matters, but deplore the license and
free practice of pre- and extra-marital sex relations which has
accompanied it. This is a case, of course, where mores do not
establish good because they conflict with biblical and moral
standards of good.

On the other hand, suppose I determine that the basis for

certain decisions for "good" are based on mere mores. Does this mean that ethics is not then involved? By no means. Here I think I must apply as nearly as I can Paul's teaching about the weaker brother.[4] Although personally I may see no clearer good in one certain practice than in another, if my community does, then, I think, the ethics of social sanction applies. What I am suggesting is an ethical "rank-ordering."

While careful discernment of the basis of a certain good may help me somewhat in understanding the force of the imperative, it helps only slightly in pinpointing an acceptable concept of good. Statements like "good is that which enhances the welfare of man" seem to be merely restating the question. H. Schwarz has helped me here:

God's intentions and activities resulted once in the basic structure of the world as his creation. They endow the world in its present form with meaning and they direct it to future fulfillment. In the same way God created man as a God-responsible being and endowed him with a life-preserving and pleasure-providing environment which is as perishable as man.

Accordingly, biogenetic endeavors should lead to an increase in the specific characteristics of man: the ability to reflect upon himself and upon his environment, and to attain the possibility of an increased responsiveness and responsibility.[5]

For purposes of this discussion, let me use as my criterion for the good of an event in human genetics Schwarz's suggestion that good is that which increases a man's responsiveness to Christ and/or his responsibility under him.

GENETIC ISSUES

I now propose to select certain areas of advance and potential in genetics, try to emphasize areas requiring current or presumptive decision making, find parallels (if possible) in current practices, apply ethical rank-ordering and see if I can indeed come close enough to a decision to vote intelligently on the issue.

Some of these issues Anderson, as a genetic counselor, deals with every day. I do not know how my amateur assessment will match up with his as a professional. I am simply trying to see how I come out, in the hope that I will actually be making some ethical decisions in science, decisions which previously I have dodged. I suspect that from time to time you will pull up short and say, "Whoa, Cassel, Huh-uh! You don't drag me into that one—at least not that way." As Professor Nash has indicated, the many facets of some of these problems make consistent decisions difficult, if not impossible—but I will try.

ETHICAL DECISIONS IN REPRODUCTIVE CONTROL
Reproductive control may mean either bringing about certain genetic combinations or preventing them from taking place. This is *selection*. When Hitler advocated and actually tried forced selection, we recoiled in horror. But why? For one thing, gross manipulation of humans, particularly reproducing humans, counters biblical principles of the family, home and love. We reject it at many levels. We also reject the tampering with an individual's freedom of choice, whether it is done by Hitler or by Skinner.[6]

H. J. Muller was a strong advocate of sperm banks as a means of improving our gene pool.[7] Sperm may be stored for several reasons. I see the ethical decisions lying more in the use made of the sperm than in the ethics of storage, although Anderson raises some interesting questions about commercialization. But what about the ultimate use of the sperm? In the first place, is artificial insemination of humans ethical in any event? As far as I know, the Bible does not mention it, although some have suggested that the levirate law that a man should marry the widow of his childless brother may have some relevancy in at least not negating the principle.[8]

I have trouble formulating a moral principle to guide me. The law allows it. It is customary practice in animal breeding but as yet relatively rare in human society. A couple having trouble producing a child by natural means might feel that their responsiveness to Christ and Christian responsibility would be enhanced by having a child to raise in the nurture and admonition of the Lord. They might also feel that artificial insemination is preferable to outright adoption. Fulfillment for both parents may be found in the process of building a family from the start. What are the alternatives?

1. If the husband's sperm can be used—no problem.

2. If not, the use of donor sperm can be considered semi-adoption. When this is understood and accepted by both husband and wife—no problem, at least no immediate problem. But in the event that the child thus produced should be defective or have undesirable traits (no matter what the reason) a basis for conflict and concurrent loss of responsiveness on the part of one or both partners is possible: "You talked me into it!" "We shouldn't have done it." The same problems may arise with full adoption I am sure, but the uncustomary nature of artificial insemination and its association with animal practices demand adjustments not inherent in full adoption. At least parents can see the child before full adoption procedures are consummated. I, personally, see no inherent ethical problem in the practice itself, but the agreement should be entered into with great understanding and extreme caution.

3. If the couple decides to use donor sperm, how is the sperm chosen? What are the ethical considerations in Muller's suggestion that, instead of using the sperm of an unknown but presumably healthy donor obtained by the administering physician, the couple shop for a sperm presumably bearing the genetic traits they most desire. I see here at least two ethical decisions. On the one hand, wisdom would seem to dictate the use of the "best" sperm possible. I am not sure our genetic knowledge is such that we can really assess the quality of a sperm, but the chances are presumed better if the donor is a gifted person than otherwise. On the other hand, if the particular sperm fertilizing the egg should bear the "ungifted" half of the donor's genes, I see the potential for greater disappointment and ultimate conflict should the child turn out poorly. Again caution is indicated.

4. Should the husband be potent, but have an identifiable undesirable genetic trait, particularly one produced by a homozygous condition (with both of the genes alike, so that a gene for this particular trait is all he has to contribute to the union) would it not be irresponsible to pass along this condition? Therefore, he should make sure his wife's ova are not exposed to his sperm.

A decision the rest of us may have to make, however, is whether any particular trait may be so socially undesirable that we are willing to restrict the freedom of mating to the individual in which such a trait is expressed. Many others in which the trait is recessive may go unidentified and hence mate freely. Such restrictions on homozygotes have proved remarkably unsuccessful in contributing to the purity of the gene pool but can often prevent the union of two homozygous individuals. I personally think I would opt for legislating social sanctions, thus making them legal sanctions in cases of this nature—even though such laws are highly discriminatory. In such cases, I see no reason why artificial insemination would not be a reasonable alternative for the couple, providing the trait is not one which would make the father a poor parent.

5. I have more trouble, I must admit, with putting the shoe on the other foot, and I do not think my problem is simply an expression of my male chauvinism. Should the female be unable to bear children, what are the possible ethical solutions? Consider two situations.

First, true impotency. The woman cannot produce viable ova, but might otherwise be able to carry the child. Artificial insemination of a donor with the husband's sperm and then a transplant so that the wife becomes her own "brood mother" would seem as ethical as artificial insemination for semi-adoption. A variation has recently been reported successful—an ovary transplant! The genetic problem is the same since the ova bear the donor's genes.

Second, not impotent but the wife is physically unable to bear children. The transplant in this case would go the other way. The hiring of a "brood mother" has further complications in that the total involvement of a third party is required even though she remains anonymous to the donors. Could the experience possibly bring all three to a more responsive and responsible relationship with Christ? In this situation I think Stob's criterion of privacy would be one factor to consider. Although I suppose an affirmative answer to my question is not unthinkable, outright adoption would seem better.

6. Personally I reject, as too mechanistic and fraught with too many dangers, both known and unknown, Muller's dream that a couple agree to "shop" at a sperm bank for the traits they want in their child or to perpetuate the genes of a great man. I prefer, I think, my "brave new world" to be "heaven."

7. Should our technique become so refined (as no doubt it will) that nuclear transplants are possible in human ova, so that a couple can order a child with a known gene complement (that of its donor), I would vote against the practice. We have no reason to presume that a nucleus from Billy Graham would eventually provide another great evangelist. Studies of identical twins, the nearest parallel, have developed ambiguous data, I believe, particularly in the area of the relative influence of "nurture and nature"—environment and genetics.

MORE PROBLEMS

This analysis has been tedious and studiedly so. I hope I have not made too many goofs or stepped on Anderson's toes too often. I am sure he has experienced many more problems in his counseling than I can think of. But I have done what I have for two reasons: (1) to suggest that making rational ethical decisions is hard work (it is no wonder we dodge making them) and (2) to make my reasoning an example for discussion.

We might go through many other genetically related problems the same way. Important as the issue is to the well-being of our environment, I purposely have not touched on reproductive control for population reduction. Contrary to my own practice, I tell my students, "Have one—adopt one."

We have all been alluding to the ethical issues in abortion. I think I can make a case for *or* against "abortion"—all the way from preventing conception by abstinence through various contraceptive practices to euthanasia of physical or genetical aberrant individuals of any age. It all depends on what definition of *man* you let me use.

The "glass uterus" problem is related. I feel that tissue culture of human tissue is highly necessary and hence good, that is, *ethical.* I am not *rationally* disturbed by flushing the experimental tissue down the drain when the experiment is completed, even if it is organized at that time in the form of a fetus. But I expect some of you are, and, to be candid, as I write this I feel *emotions* that would probably make the needle on a lie detector jump. We need to explore the relative roles of *reason* and *emotion* in making ethical decisions and to investigate the action of *conscience.*

Genetic engineering and genetic surgery is another critical developing field.[9] I tend to make my ethical decisions here parallel the decisions I would make regarding gross surgery. Corrective surgery for the preservation or greater comfort of an individual is humanitarian. Preventive medicine is even more desirable for the individual. But two deeper problems bother me.

One is the effects on our exploding population of improved medical techniques. The question has also been raised about the effect on our population, our way of life and our whole social structure should our life expectancy be increased twenty to twenty-five years.

The other problem is the one with which I started. When the genetic tools are in our hands by which we can practice corrective or preventive genetic engineering, we will have the tools with which to practice genetic improvement. Do you want to be a member of the committee which decides what is a better man? I hope so! I hope that this discussion, under the illumination of the Holy Spirit, will make each of us a better committee member. It is imperative that committed Christians sit on such committees.

1. *See J. Frank Cassel, "Biology," in* Christ and the Modern Mind *(Downers Grove, Ill.: InterVarsity Press, 1972), pp. 251-62.*

2. *Matthew 19:17 and 2 Corinthians 5:31 (Phillips).*

3. *Exodus 20:12-13.*

4. *See Romans 14:1-3 and 1 Corinthians 10:23—11:1.*

5. *H. Schwarz, "Theological Implications of Modern Biogenetics,"* Zygon, *5, 262.*

6. *See Crabb's and Underwager's essays in this volume.*

7. *See, for example, H. J. Muller, "Means and Aims in Human Genetic Betterment," in* The Control of Human Heredity and Evolution, *ed. T. M. Sonneburn (New York: Macmillan, 1965).*

8. *Deuteronomy 25:5-10.*

9. *See* The Control of Human Heredity.

IV
Ethics in Psychology

What's Beyond Freedom and Dignity?
by Ralph C. Underwager

N either the scientist nor the Christian need be surprised, indignant nor fearful at the proposals advanced by B. F. Skinner aimed at a more scientific and successful control of human behavior. The *scientist* need not be surprised, for the proposals advanced are simply the logical extension of the ideology of science from matter to man. He need not be indignant, for if there are ethical issues raised by the proposals the scientist's only function *as scientist* is to ascertain the facts of the case. He need not be fearful, for, as Skinner points out (and indeed relies upon), if the control of man is scientific there is a built-in self-correcting process that will correct any mistaken assertions of fact or ineffective methods of control.

The *Christian* need not be surprised, for the proposals represent simply another expression of what the Christian has always known—that the law rules over natural man and all of his behavior reflects the fact of his existence. The Christian need not be indignant, for he knows that whatever ethical or moral expressions men may make the Law of God is the reality that effectively makes the difference. The Christian need not be fearful, for the proposals, insofar as they reflect the Law and its judgment, merely prepare the way for the proclamation of the gospel. It is my thesis that for the Christian the rigorous application of empiricism to human life positively affects his primary goal—the proclamation of the Gospel so as to glorify God. In the course of this paper these are the propositions which I propose to develop.

CHRISTIAN ORTHODOXY AND SCIENTIFIC CLAIMS

It is generally assumed that the position of the strict behaviorist or logical empiricist is diametrically opposed to that of the orthodox Christian. What could be more plain than that the relativist or subjectivist view of ethical issues (whether utilitarian, intuitionist, pragmatist, etc.) is opposed to the absolutist, eternal, revealed uncompromising ethical position associated with the Christian church? If utilitarianism, pragmatism, the emotive theory, etc., are too human and relativistic for the Christian, how much more unacceptable is the view that moral or ethical assertions are simply ineffective attempts to control other people. This view, which classifies "Genocide is evil" with "I prefer blondes," surely is in radical opposition to the claim that, for instance, divorce is always, everywhere, in-and-of-itself wrong, regardless of the consequences and the human suffering involved.

But absolutist-relativist is only one way to cut the question of the relationship between Christian orthodoxy, ethics and alleged scientific claims. The history of this attempt to understand the relationship indicates that it may not be a very fruitful one at that. It hardly has occurred to anyone to ask whether orthodox Christianity might in fact benefit from the orthodox positivist or subjectivist-relativist line about ethics and the claim that science can control human behavior. I believe that Christianity can benefit.

Before developing the way in which the proposals of Skinner and the attendant ethical claims, willy-nilly, redound to the benefit of the Christian, I shall treat the relationship of science and scientists to the ethical implications of scientific control of human behavior. It seems to me that there are only four possible positions regarding the relationship between science and ethics. First, science may be seen as purely objective, concerned not at all with questions of value or ethics but only with neutral description and discovery of fact. For a long time this was the dominant claim of science, though it is no longer heard quite as often as it once was. On this view the scientist makes no ethical judgments but pursues truth wherever it leads him. The result of this approach appears to be clearly that science serves any master, disclaiming any responsibility for the results of its efforts. Sen. McGovern, in describing the scientific establishment used the following limerick:

> There once was a lady from Trent
> Who said that she knew what it meant
> When men took her to dine
> Bought her cocktails and wine
> She knew what it meant—but she went.

A second position regarding science and ethics is to assert that questions of ethics and value enter in at the beginning of the scientific venture in terms of determining what questions are asked, what priorities are established and so on. If this is the case, then the scientist as scientist has no particular claim to expertise in value or ethical judgments and ought indeed seek the counsel of the ethical expert before beginning his scientific task. Once he begins his scientific work, again his function is to ascertain fact.

A third position is that the scientist throughout his scientific work is functioning as a choosing, valuing, ethically responsible person. This leaves the scientist in the morass of subjectivism and no longer a scientist.

The fourth position, again one which has been powerfully expressed in the history of science, is that science will itself build ethics scientifically by the application of science to ethical questions. This is Skinner's position, really. In describing the design for cultural engineering based upon science, he clearly anticipates that the self-correcting nature of the scientific method will result in the solution of any and all ethical questions that have ever been asked.

In all four of these positions there is nothing inherent that science can contribute in the doing of science beyond the gathering of fact. The only question which the scientist qua scientist can ask Skinner is, "How good are your observations, data and methods? Do you explain, predict and control successfully?" So long as Skinner meets the canons of scientific methodology in his work, his proposals for the scientific control of human behavior cannot be ethically rejected by the scientist qua scientist. If an individual scientist chooses to object to Skinner's proposals on ethical grounds, he does so not as a scientist but as an ethical animal on all fours with all other ethical animals including Skinner.

If the scientist objects on ethical grounds to Skinner's proposals for control, Skinner need only reply, as he has done interminably since the early 50s, "Look at the results. My proposals will bring better results than you have been able to get, and here is the evidence." An eminently scientific response that can be challenged only on the basis of data, not ethics, for it is most difficult to find an ethical base to challenge the vision of happy, well-adjusted human beings busily engaged in productive, creative and rewarding activities. If an appeal is made to the autonomy of the individual, Skinner need only reply exactly as he has in his book *Beyond Freedom and Dignity:* "Look at the results! An autonomous, free man of dignity has produced the world we now live in. Do you want to keep it that way?"

The only point at which science as science can dispute with Skinner is on the question of his scientific rigor. Indeed, this is currently being done within psychology. A significant body of research is developing which supports a cognitive, information-processing view of human behavior. The vulnerability of Skinner's proposals scientifically lies in establishing that they do not work, that his prescriptions for control are as ineffective as those he criticizes. Here, too, however, the scientist has nothing to contribute as scientist beyond the falsification of Skinner's claims to have adequately explained, predicted and controlled the variables of interest to his scientific domain.

THE SCIENTIST IN THE ETHICAL ARENA
If a scientist enters the ethical arena to do battle with Skinner

or anyone elso on ethical issues, I believe he is subject to the devastating critique of logical empiricism regarding ethical issues. Let me briefly review that critique, using the position advanced by Ayer: ". . . So far as statements of value are significant, they are ordinary 'scientific' statements; and that insofar as they are not scientific, they are not in the literal sense significant, but are simply expressions of emotion which can be neither true nor false." Insofar as they are neither true nor false, the radical empiricist critique runs, they are literally non-sense, meaningless. This critique effectively eliminates ethics as an area of dispute, in the following way.

First, moral disputes are almost always problems in casuistry. Casuistry, like law, logic and the rules of badminton, consists in setting one set of statements (for example, descriptions of subject Smith's acts) alongside another set of statements, namely, the rules of ethical system E_1. If they match, Smith is behaving ethically. If they do not match, Smith is behaving immorally.

Ideally, the rules of ethical system E_1 are axiomatized and free of contradictions. That there are large numbers of moral disputes regarding the match between described behavior and the rules only indicates that ethical system E_1 has not been clearly axiomatized yet, but does not signify that, in principle, ethical system E_1 cannot be axiomatized clearly and without contradiction. A distressing but not impossible state of affairs.

In situations where the moral dispute is not a problem of casuistry but rather a disagreement between ethical systems E_1 and E_2, the dispute is resolved like this: Given a concrete situation where the antagonists agree upon the physical-social situation, either the proponent of E_1 demonstrates a contradiction within system E_2, or the antagonists finally simply agree to disagree. For me "good" or "right" or "ought" means conforming to E_1, but for you it means conforming to E_2. Thus the dispute is semantic only, involving a different systematic use of ethical primitives like "good," "wrong" or "ought."

If I use "ought" with a grammar system exhibited by system E_1 while you use "ought" with a different grammar shown in system E_2, then there simply is no cognitive disagreement. We both describe the same facts, we even agree on whether your theorems or mine can be matched up with the facts. Hence we can also agree that a given concrete act "ought" to be done in E_1 and E_2 respectively. But there is no way in which E_1 and E_2 can logically conflict. If a person appeals to *feeling* guilty or innocent in either E_1 or E_2, then, as Ayer avers, he is in the domain of scientific psychology, and all ethical quandries can be investigated and solved by application of the science of psychology to discover when and under what circumstances men feel guilty or innocent. This is precisely what Skinner proposes, insofar as he deals with ethical questions. Having discovered when and under what circumstances men feel guilty or innocent, one simply manipulates the reinforcers appropriately to establish and maintain control.

As to the question of control, there are several points which it seems advisable to make here. I am sure we agree that men—as individuals and as societies—have always endeavored to understand, predict, influence and control human behavior, both their own and that of others. I believe we agree that the behavioral sciences are making and will continue to make increasingly rapid progress in the understanding of behavior. With increased understanding the capacity to predict and control human behavior will develop as rapidly. I believe we also agree that a science of human behavior is both a valid and possible scientific pursuit, whose potential is quite powerful. As Robert Oppenheimer told the American Psychological Association in 1956, the problems that psychologists will pose for society by their growing ability to control human behavior will be much more grave than the problems posed by the ability of physicists to control the reactions of matter.

What are the issues, then? They can be stated very briefly. Who will be controlled? Who will be the controllers? What type of control will be exercised? Toward what end (or goal), purpose or value will control be exercised? Now we are back in the area of ethics and solidly contained in Ayer's box that ethical systems cannot be anything other than meaningless except within the confines of an axiomatized system. Disputes between systems are semantic in nature and cannot logically be a matter of dispute. This leaves us with the grim prospect that neither science nor ethics can establish persuasive answers to the issues of control. In the end, then, it would appear from history that decisions will be made through the political process through the use of power. In view of both history and the present situation in politics, this is hardly a prospect to evoke enthusiasm.

ONE CHRISTIAN'S PERSPECTIVE

But, you may ask, what of religion? What of Christianity? What stance does the Christian take toward these issues? Here I must declare my own theological bias. I am by choice and training committed to the theological tradition of Lutheranism, and I will draw upon that tradition to delineate a Christian response to the situation set forth thus far. As such, it really is only my own personal response. I cannot claim that all Lutherans or even a majority of Lutherans, much less Lutheran theologians, would agree with me.

What is Christianity? It is not ethics. The Christian faith is by no means identical with an ethical system nor is its primary concern to inculcate ethical or moral values. Its primary concern is the response of faith to the proclamation of the Gospel that in Jesus Christ atonement, forgiveness and newness of life is given to men freely and unconditionally by a God who graciously loves men. That response of faith includes the continued proclamation of this good news to other Christians and to all men. In the service of that continued proclamation, I hold that current developments in the control of human behavior and the ineffectiveness of ethics to answer the questions raised by these developments are a positive help to the Christian. How can this be?

Lutheran theology has long maintained that the key to the Christian life is the proper discrimination between Law and Gospel. Research I have done into the beliefs, values, attitudes and behavior of Lutherans established that these are not simply abstruse, esoteric theological constructs, but represent two polarities that dramatically and decisively shape both beliefs and behavior. I suggest that it is nomological existence, that is, life under the Law, that is basic to science, ethics and the issue of control. Science as a human endeavor, ethics as a human endeavor and even Skinner's proposals as a human endeavor are nothing more than the working of the Law in human existence to accomplish the purpose of the Law "that every mouth may be stopped and all the world may become guilty before God" (Rom. 3:19).

How does the Law do this? In the first place it is the Law that establishes the basic contingent relationship upon which science, ethics and all natural human experience is built. And it is the conditional promise of the Law, "I the Lord your God . . . show steadfast love to thousands of those who love me and keep my commandments" (Ex. 20:5-6), that establishes the simple if-then quality of human experience. Reward is contingent upon behavior exactly as in Skinner's operant conditioning model.

Second, the Law contains, in precise coordination with the promise and expectation of reward, a threat of punishment. It is always a law of retribution, for good as well as for ill. The law of retribution is God's Law in the strictest sense; man in every case is only the executor who carries it out. "Vengeance is mine. I will repay," says God. Nomological existence, life under the Law, means to live in a contingent world under the curse of God's wrath.

This is what separates the Law of God from ethics. Ethics is the application of a set of rules to a given situation. The Law of God is not simply rules for life, an ethical system, that operates to determine questions of good or evil, right or wrong. The Law, if it is seen as simply an ethical system, then functions like an ethical system only, to define transgressions and good works. It is like a fence running alongside a straight path. We travel this path through life, obviously on the right side of the fence but occasionally or even frequently jumping over it to cavort capriciously on the wrong side. When this is drawn to our attention by the application of the rules, we obediently step back onto the right side and behave ethically until the next episode.

In reality the Law has a much different task. It does not operate with the assumption that we are on this side of the fence. Rather, it tells us that we are already over the fence and that our entire life's journey from beginning to end is on the wrong side of the fence. This represents that actual meaning of the church's doctrine of original sin. We are from the very beginning in the wrong territory. Paul makes the same point in his statement that the Law was not given until 430 years after Abraham (Gal. 3:17). He means, of course, the Decalogue. On the other hand, sin was present long before Sinai. Consequently death, too, reigned from Adam to Moses. Accordingly, the divine verdict upon men was already given. From Adam to the present, men are not only judged by God but also condemned and sentenced by him. The Sinaitic legislation in no sense produced a turn for the better by giving men a rule for life, by which they could organize their lives. Instead it revived sin, granting it new power by provoking it to opposition: ". . . Moreover the law entered that the sin might abound" (Rom. 5:20). And, ". . . sin, taking occasion by the commandment, wrought in me all manner of concupiscence. For without the law sin was dead . . . but when the commandment came, sin revived and I died" (Rom. 7:8-9).

The Lutheran confessions assert *Lex semper accusat,* "the Law always accuses." If the Law is really God's Law, God never assumes the attitude of the human legislator merely waiting to see whether or how a man will fulfill it. Rather, God is always the judge who has rendered a verdict and, without making any exceptions, passed sentence. No amount of thoughtful reflection or ethical clarification can eliminate this accusatory work of the Law, not so long as man remains mortal. It functions this way for every individual, for the godless as well as for the so-called righteous, and also for the regenerate. What it does is to place all of us in the impossible bind that we cannot be what we are (sinful), we must be what we cannot be (perfect).

That science has come to the point of advocating scientific control of human behavior using the paradigm of reward and punishment set up by the Law of God is the first step in the positive benefit to the orthodox Christian of applying a rigorous scientific empiricism to human life. Skinner is, in reality, forced by the Law, whether he wills it or not, like Baalam's ass to bray to the world the Word of God, "You are guilty!" The logical empiricist critique of ethics, which makes it impossible for any ethical system to claim preeminence in answering the problems posed by the issue of scientific control of human behavior, also serves the Law's purpose of accusing men, of shutting up every mouth that all the world may be guilty.

The Law fulfills still another function. Law is a concept of order, denoting a particular relationship of man to God, as well as to the entire creaturely world. By means of creation, man is placed into the world. By means of Law he is held secure in it. He is not at the mercy of an arbitrary, capricious, indeterminate chaos. He lives in an orderly world where there is regularity and commonality. It is this function of the Law which ordinary science depends upon for its life.

However, the nomological order of the world is in danger of being disturbed or destroyed by the powers of evil. There also exists in the world an order of evil with its own nomological structure—the reign of sin (Rom. 5:21; 6:12-23), which has its own psychological law (Rom. 7:7-25; Jas. 1:15), sociological law (2 Kings 17:22), hereditary law (Rom. 5:29), law of tradition (2 Kings 3:3; 10:29) and law of accumulation (Is. 30:1). The most dreadful of these laws of evil is the law of demonization. We call an event demonic in which good is transformed into evil. In these days it is noteworthy that the question about the demonic aspect of science is being seriously raised. The extent to which both the consequences of scientific knowledge and its application to human life (whether through the medium of Skinner or through ecological disasters) raise the issue of man's evil in the midst of his highest accomplishments of science can only further sharpen the accusatory impact of the Law, "You are guilty!"

According to Romans 13, God has established the order of the state to hold in check, even by use of force, the forces of evil within the order of the world. The state is God's agent administering the law of retribution. To that extent political control of the science of human behavior may be seen as God's way of holding potential evil, in its application to human life, within the limits of security. This accomplishes no more, however, than preserving the nomological order only externally. Against internal law-breaking which can be camouflaged by externally good behavior, the entire nomological order is unable to provide any defense. It is this latter fact which the questions raised by the possibility of the scientific control of human behavior lays bare before our eyes.

For the orthodox Christian the autonomous man of freedom and dignity against which Skinner brings the weight of science has never existed. The concept of a free, autonomous man possessing dignity, honor, integrity and goodness is a humanistic myth. That myth can be propounded only when the accusatory function of the Law is not seen, when the Law is seen purely as a legislative rule of life like any other ethical system. The myth of man's freedom and dignity is what places him on the right side of the fence, portraying him as only occasionally getting on the wrong side and needing to be reminded by the rules to get back on the right side. The extent to which the scientific behavioristic attack upon that myth of man's freedom and dignity succeeds in exposing man's true condition—in bondage to corruption and evil, totally on the wrong side of the fence from the beginning to the end of life—to that extent the Christian is helped both in his own life and his labor to proclaim the gospel.

When I was taught how to preach, I was taught that it is appropriate to declare the Law and its accusation first, that the Law in its judging and condemning thrust prepares a man for Christ. Paul says that the Law is God's schoolmaster to bring us to Christ. As a preacher, I can only say three cheers for Skinner. He is preaching one of the most powerful statements of the accusatory function of the Law that I have yet heard. I rather expect that the more people hear clearly what he is saying, the more openness and readiness there will be to hear the word of God's grace. Go to it, Skinner!

THE QUESTIONS ABOUT CONTROL

But how are we going to settle the questions about the control of human behavior? Suppose that we actually institute Skinner's program of cultural engineering. Then what? How do we determine who is to be the controller and who the controlled? How do we determine the goal, end or purpose of the control? I suggest that the first step for the Christian is to reinforce the ethical positivism of both Ayer and Skinner.

So we get to the point then in the discussion, when we have clarified that you are an E_1 man and I am an E_2 man. We are fully enlightened about the axiomatic character of each other's ethical system, and we have clarified that our ought-impulses and our guilt-feelings are geared into different grammars and that there is indeed no cognitive dispute about that. If I then say, "Your choice for controller and for goal is wrong," whether this is a communication depends upon whether it is wrong in both E_1 and E_2. If it is, the remark is complete communication and we can go on to a further choice. If it is not, the remark is ambiguous. I should say, rather, "Your choice is wrong$_1$," which again is complete communication. We can both believe it.

Of course, if I say, "Your choice is wrong$_2$," I also fully expect you to admit it since we are both cognitively clear on E_1 and E_2. I do not, however, expect you to feel guilt nor any impulsion or motivation to change your choice. Feeling guilty and changing conduct are in the pragmatic grammar of ought$_1$ and ought$_2$, and these grammars differ. You, on the other hand, being perfectly clear on the grammar of E_1 and E_2, do expect me to feel disapproval of your choice which is clearly wrong$_2$.

Do you expect me to disapprove of you as well as of your choice? This depends upon my meta-ethics and your understanding of them. If I am a tough pharisaical pietist, then you do expect me to disapprove of you as well as of your choice. But then you probably disapprove of me, too, and so we are even. But feelings do not change anything. To have a feeling geared to a word or a classification of a given act is not an assertion that has meaning, except insofar as it is subject to the science of psychology, and then we are back without any means of determining between E_1 and E_2, except through the very way we are trying to work out, that is, the scientific control of human behavior.

So here we sit with our ethical grammars E_1 and E_2, implicitly defining ought$_1$ and ought$_2$ respectively. We are cognitively clear, and we both realize that the different pragmatic gearing-ins of our concrete ought-impulsions, resulting from the different roles of ought$_1$ and ought$_2$ in E_1 and E_2, do not constitute cognitive differences but only semantic ones and cannot be significantly disputed about. We are now ready to go beyond the concepts of freedom and dignity and autonomous man and scientific control of mechanistic man.

Now I bring in this claim. I say, "Incidentally, system E_2 has another interesting non-formal property, in which you might be interested. Let me tell you about it. The Creator of you and me and all things has communicated E_2 to mankind, and has commanded that it is obligatory$_2$. God's ethical grammar is my E_2 and not your E_1. Furthermore, E_2 is a subsystem of a vastly more complex and larger system, E_G, much of which is not known to us. However, that should not surprise us, God being what he is and we being what we are."

You may reply, "Well, granting for the moment that what you say is true, I still do not see why I should repudiate E_1 for E_2." To which I reply, "Oh, I am not suggesting that you repudiate E_1. Go ahead and use it to classify acts wrong$_1$ or right$_1$ as you will. After all, we understand perfectly that we have two grammars. I was merely adding to your store of empirical knowledge about E_2." Then we may go on to discuss the factual, empirical claim, a significant area, that will allow for something other than fruitless and interminable ethical disputes that are settled only on the basis of political power.

Along the way, I will interject a further empirical claim about system E_G, namely, that there is an arrangement, a commitment from the Creator to love us; that he has shown and demonstrated that love concretely and specifically in the person, work, death and resurrection of Jesus Christ. I will tell you the good news about the Gospel. So then, what am I actually inviting you to do about E_1 and E_2, in our attempt to settle the ethical questions centering around the scientific control of human behavior? Your impulsions, conduct and guilt-feelings are now geared to E_1 rather than E_2. I give you the further empirical information about E_2. It is a psychological fact that if you believe this genuinely, you will experience a change in your pragmatic gearing-ins of impulsions, ought-feelings and conduct. Your behavior will change.

But how has this approach been helped by the addition of ethical positivism? To the contemporary mind, many learned cliches immediately come to mind when one speaks of Christianity which reflect the fact that the Gospel is a scandal and an offense to the natural man, to the man living under nomological existence. They need not all be mentioned here, but some of them are the claims of atonement dependent upon the shedding of blood, original sin and the injustice of divine election. Logical positivism applied to ethics or the radical behaviorism of Skinner applied to ethics takes all the sting out of this. It is no longer possible for a contemporary man to see this as merely an exercise in futility or to take offense at it. Ayer has drawn the teeth from man's moral indignation at the God of the Old Testament or the New, while Skinner has confronted men with the immediate practical bankruptcy of his ethical positions.

THE CHRISTIAN WITHOUT THE LAW
Suppose that we get to the point of the acceptance of the

Gospel. Let's say conversion occurs and Jesus is believed as Lord and Savior. Then what of the issue of the control of human behavior? The Law is removed from a Christian. But how is he supposed to live without the Law? Is it not needed to tell him what he should be doing? Will he not just become wildly permissive and libertine if he doesn't have the Law? Once I have used E_2 to get to the place where the proclamation of the Gospel has had its effect and brought newness of life, do I then really discard E_2? Do ethical questions become of no concern?

The answer of the Gospels is clear. Wherever the Holy One of God enters, the demons become speechless (Mk. 1:24). Jesus is Master and Lord. He is the personal measure for all things, including the control of human behavior by scientific techniques. Jesus is the measure of doing, abstaining, loving and suffering. The disciple of Jesus no longer needs be told that he ought not to practice idolatry, commit adultery or imperiously seek to impose a utopia upon his fellow men. He no longer has any need for the Law's promises or threats, its rewards or punishments. His life and existence have moved into the non-contingent sphere. Even as God's love for him in Christ is non-contingent, unconditioned, gracious and free, he now walks in the newness of life.

For what purpose does a child of God still need the Law, since his distinctive trademark is precisely in his being "led by the Spirit" (Rom. 8:14)? It is not the spirit of fear that he has received (2 Tim. 1:7), so why should he still live in fear of the Law's threats, even of its threat to exercise control? That is no different from what the Law has always done and what it had been doing in his life before he was brought into light. The scientific control advocated by Skinner is nothing more or less for a Christian than what he had previously been living under, the bondage of the Law. Now in Christ he is freed from that bondage. It has no more power over him and it cannot affect his life in Christ.

Now that the meditation of the Spirit enables him to understand the gifts bestowed by God, namely, grace (1 Cor. 2:12) how could he still raise claims for any rewards? What purpose can the Law have for those who walk by the Spirit and thus are freed and protected from the desires of the flesh (Gal. 5:16), for those who work miracles by the Spirit (Gal. 3:5), for those whom the Spirit teaches how to pray (Rom. 8:26; Gal. 4:6), for those in whom the Spirit brings forth love, which not only fulfills the entire Law but produces more than the Law can ever demand—joy, peace, faithfulness (Gal. 5:22)? No, he has not received the Spirit by the works of the Law (Gal. 3:2) and because he is under the Spirit's rule he is therefore no longer under the Law (Gal. 5:18). Just as Law and Grace stand in opposition to each other, so it is with Law and Spirit. The Law is bondage (Gal. 3:23), the Spirit freedom (2 Cor. 3:17).

To sum up, the ethical questions raised by the proposal for the scientific control of human behavior can be settled neither by ethical discussions, as the logical positivists have demonstrated, nor by the practice of science, for it is that practice itself which brings about the ethical issues. My proposal is that it is the political power, as God's agent to control evil, which will, in fact, determine the questions centering around the scientific control of human behavior. In either event, the raising of the issue for the orthodox Christian represents a powerful aid in his ability to proclaim the Gospel of Jesus Christ. The clear and forthright proclamation of the Law in which Skinner is engaged makes it possible for the Christian to witness and to proclaim the good news of the Gospel.

Beyond or Beneath
Freedom and Dignity
by Lawrence J. Crabb

I n developing a Christian response to B. F. Skinner, it is helpful to separate three aspects of his work; first, his philosophical position, most thoroughly presented in his latest book *Beyond Freedom and Dignity*; second, the research data upon which he bases his utopian system; and third, the validity of the inductive jump from the data to his philosophical conclusions.

Skinner's philosophy needs to be baldly and simply stated. According to Skinner himself, "What is being abolished is autonomous man."[1] Man is totally and completely controlled by his environment. There is nothing in man, there is no "you"; there is just a group of conditioned responses. What appears to be freely chosen behavior is really inconspicuously controlled behavior. Man is neither free nor significant. Skinner's utopia essentially consists of a world which uses behavioral technology to control all human behavior in ways which promote the survival of the human species.

Francis Schaeffer, in *Back to Freedom and Dignity,* a recent book discussing man's significance, argues against Skinner's philosophy by pointing out four crucial questions[2] for which Skinner can have no adequate answer and still remain Skinnerian:

1. Who will control the persons who arrange the environment which controls everyone else?

2. How does one determine the boundary between what man

can do with available knowledge and what man *should* do? Along the same line, C. S. Lewis has suggested that man's sense of "oughtness" cannot be adequately accounted for within a naturalistic system. In order to decide what we ought to do with what we know, we must go outside Skinner's system.

3. Within Skinnerian philosophy, how can anything be defended as a value? This question follows naturally from the previous one. What we ought to do depends upon our values. Skinner's value system, at his own insistence, reduces to the primary value of survival. But in the absence of an objective, extra-human morality, one is left with DeSade's conclusion that "What is is right." Schaeffer argues that a closed philosophy which shuts man up to man reduces man to zero, the accidental result of the impersonal plus time plus chance. The word *value* becomes no more than noise.

4. Finally, if (as Skinner asserts) man has been wrong for so long in his observation that he has a peculiar quality of "man-nishness" which separates him from non-man, how can we ever really trust any man's thinking, including Skinner's?

These four unanswered questions serve to point out the element of faith in Skinner's alleged scientific philosophy and succeed, in my thinking, in demonstrating that even Skinner cannot live in complete consistency with Skinnerian philosophy. Argument against Skinner's final philosophy, however, does not directly bear upon either the inductive steps from his data to his philosophy or the research findings themselves.

FROM DATA TO DOGMA

Before I consider what I believe to be a Christian understanding of Skinner's data, let me briefly comment on the inductive jump from data to dogma. It cannot be denied that Skinner is able to explain, predict and control a great deal of outcome variance in human behavior by means of operant conditioning. In other words, by carefully arranging a temporal contingency between a response and a positive reinforcer, he is able to point to a significant change in the frequency of behavior which the reinforcer follows. As Skinner himself puts it, "When a bit of behavior is followed by a certain consequence, it is more likely to occur again, and a consequence having this effect is called a reinforcer."[3] Harold McKay cogently argues that the conclusion that all behavior is therefore completely controlled by its consequences is an error of inductive generalization. To suggest that the behavioristic perspective is somehow basic and exhausts the ultimately true statements that may be made about the causes of human behavior is to fall prey to what McKay terms the fallacy of "nothing-buttery": Nothing but his analysis is true.

A further problem with Skinner's inductive conclusion that man is a responding, never-initiating organism involves the imperfection of empirical prediction and control. The always present degree of inaccuracy in prediction and the incompleteness in control may be explained in two very different ways. A scientist who a priori rejects free will will argue, as Skinner does, that scientific methodology has simply not yet attained the sophistication necessary to isolate the rest of the controlling variables. Skinner states that "Personal exemption from a complete determinism is revoked as scientific analysis progresses, particularly in accounting for the behavior of the individual."

But scientific analysis has not progressed to the point of perfect prediction. That fact leaves the door open to the possibility that some portion of the unpredicted effects are the direct function of independent choice, a sort of "stubborn cussedness" in man which refuses to relinquish all claim to significance and autonomy. Increasingly sensitive methodology may pick up more of the controlling factors but whether there will always and necessarily be some unpredictable variance resulting from the incurable stubborn cussedness of man is, in the absence of perfect empirical prediction, a scientifically unanswerable question. Skinner is therefore premature in asserting that his inductive leap from the data of much control to the conclusion of no autonomy is logically and scientifically justified.

BIBLICAL PERSPECTIVE ON CONTINGENT BEHAVIOR

Even after one has satisfied his mind that neither Skinner's philosophy nor his inductive strategy pose a real intellectual threat to biblical thinking, there still remains the job of accounting for Skinner's well-documented assertion that much of human behavior is in fact controlled by its consequences. Can the biblical view of man as a significant, moral and responsible being be reconciled with Skinner's observation that man often behaves in apparently automatic response to his environment? God set Adam the task of subduing nature and gave him the autonomy from nature necessary for the job. Skinner has good evidence that the tables have turned and nature now largely controls man. Skinner, of course, goes on to make his inductive leap that man is now and always has been nothing more than a billiard ball moving only as it is moved by an outside force. The Scriptures hold man accountable for his movement, suggesting some real measure of self-direction. The problem then is to see if Skinner's research findings that much of our behavior is under external control can be gracefully integrated with a biblical conception of man as a significant, free, choosing being.

The beginning of the solution is found in Schaeffer's observation that only Christianity presents a God who is both infinite and personal. The polytheism of ancient Egypt and Greece offered gods who were personal, that is, who possessed personality and could therefore relate meaningfully to man, but who were in every case limited. Many of the modern religions, particularly the Eastern mystical systems, offer a god who is infinite but impersonal, more of an "it" than a "he." Terms like Cosmic Being and Transcendent Otherness are used to describe their impersonal yet pantheistically infinite god. Biblical Christianity, by contrast, asserts that God is both infinite and personal. Because God is infinite, he is necessarily separate from all other creation, including man. Because God is infinite, he is a non-contingent Being. He depends on nothing external to himself for his existence.

But man is finite, and to be finite necessarily implies contingency and clearly rules out complete autonomy. Man is a contingent being, and he shares that characteristic with all other creation. He is, therefore, to at least some degree truly dependent on his environment. If he does not eat, he dies. If he remains in the sun too long, his skin burns. We are indebted to Skinner for clarifying the motivating features of man's contingent relationship to his world. Because hunger is aversive, man does things to avoid an empty stomach: He grows vegetables or works in a factory for which he receives money which he can trade for meat and milk. Because he experiences pain as unpleasant, he is motivated to come out of the sun before he gets badly sunburned. Because man is really and genuinely a part of nature from the perspective of the infinite-finite dimension, he is vulnerable to the influence of forces outside himself, just as other forms of creation, all similarly contingent, are at least partly manipulable by external agents.

Comparative and animal psychology have long been justified as relevant to human behavior on the grounds of man-animal continuity as taught by evolutionary theory. It seems to me that their validity as disciplines relevant to man can equally well be argued in terms not of evolution, but rather of man's shared status as contingent being. Behavioral psychology like Skinner's, emphasizing the universality of conditioning principles across all forms of life, would therefore be expected to offer valuable insights, since men, like animals, are influenced by the world around them. Just as a dog's behavior can be shaped by offering a bone immediately following a desired response, so a child's (or an adult's) behavior may be shaped by arranging reinforcing consequences. Skinner has said that "Man is much more than a dog, but like a dog he is within the range of scientific analysis."[4]

MAN'S PERSONALNESS

Now Christians must not retreat from the fact that at least some of our behavior is conditioned. To deny the effects of our envi-

ronment on our behavior is to fly in the face of obvious research findings and to miss the point that man is an integral part
of God's creation and as such is subject to external environmental influence.

But Skinner fails to see that man's behavior is not only more
complex than a dog's, but that man also possesses a personalness
which sets him quite apart from the dog. Man's nature cannot
be completely described in terms of the attribute of finitude
which he shares with his environment. Man, created in the
image of a personal God, is also a personal being. It is this
attribute of personalness which separates man from all other
creation by locating within man the real power of choice, the
ability to make a difference, the potential for acting on his
world rather than just being acted upon. When a personal God
who created man in his own image is posited, man immediately
becomes unique. He can think, reflect, criticize, and deliberately and consciously adapt. In short, he becomes significant by
virtue of his freedom to choose.

When this capacity for free action is not expressed, for whatever reason, man loses his uniqueness and becomes pathologi-
cally involved with his environment. I recall dealing with a
woman who was terribly sensitive to every movement, every
noise, every activity in her immediate world. The noise of the
footsteps of a person some distance away would seem to her
like a thundering herd of cattle. The filtering mechanism,
Huxley's term for that which screens out extraneous impinging
stimuli and allows us to tune in to the narrow range of relevant
stimuation, seemed to have broken down in her. Now the root
of the problem I believe was this. She believed she was completely dependent on elements in her environment (like a husband's approval) for her significance. She had lost sight of her
true significance as a free choosing being who could rise above
circumstances and enjoy a meaning and sense of personal worth
and a foundation for self-assertion based not on her relationship
to her world but on her relationship to God.

In exploring her background, it became apparent that life had lost her in the shuffle. Her husband had regarded her as less important than his mother. Her employers evidenced no concern for her needs in stressful situations. They made it distressingly clear that their interest was centered in her performance as it related to their welfare. Her family had consistently ignored her special needs and paid no attention to her pleas for notice. She later began to experience hysterical fits of uncontrollable screaming. I believe these were really a desperate plea to be heard, to be recognized, to matter. She felt like a pie cut up in several pieces. A number of people had each taken a piece until there was no person left, just an empty pie tin. She had failed to find a way to be intrinsically significant, independent of her environment. Therefore, her environment became crucially important to her. She helplessly tuned in to all of the stimulation in her environment with an uncomfortable intensity in a futile effort to find her own identity.

MENTAL HEALTH

Such an analysis has implications for the concept of *mental health*. Normal man is neither fully identified with God nor with nature. With each one he shares attributes which should be fully actualized if he is to be fully human. With nature he shares finitude or contingency and a consequent responsiveness to environmental stimulation. If that aspect is suppressed, man withdraws and lives in a non-real, private world. With God, he shares personalness. If his personalness remains unexpressed, he becomes helplessly driven by circumstance and loses his dignity as a thinking organism that can act upon his world. The mentally healthy individual is the well-balanced man who is both alert and responsive to his environment (which, of course, includes people) and confidently aware of and responsibly implementing his potential for personally influencing his world by thinking, reflecting and choosing.

Since man is finite and therefore contingent, it follows that his real personalness is also contingent and depends for its viability on a relationship to God, the source of all meaning and free action. To the degree that an individual turns away from full dependency on God, he loses the power to be independent of his environment. The fact that Skinner is able to demonstrate just how much of our behavior is manipulable by environmental contingencies need not compel us to move beyond believing in our human significance and freedom, but should cause us to admit sorrowfully that man as a race has fallen beneath his real freedom by turning away from the source of all freedom, God himself. In other words, man has relinquished part of his significance as a human being by failing to assert his potential for a personal relationship with a personal God through the Person of Jesus Christ. He has thus emphasized the contingent aspect of his being at the expense of his personal aspect; he has allowed himself to fall down to the level of all other creation and to lose much of his God-based ability to rise above circumstances. He has become less independent of his environment by becoming more independent of God.

God never intended man to be the servant of circumstance. Paul said he was content no matter what his circumstance because he could always, in the power of God's Spirit, assert himself as a free agent who had yielded fully to God. Paul exhibited the sense of balance that constitutes mental health: As a finite, contingent being, he was respectful of and responsive to his world, the world of other people (he selflessly gave his energies to help them) and the world of other things (he felt free to use them but never exploited or abused them nor let himself be used by them); as a personal being, he was in touch with the personal God and thus enjoyed the significance of true independence from his environment.

But the drift among human beings is away from God. And that explains why Skinner has found that so much of our behavior is controllable by our environment. Skinner's data are real, frighteningly real, and should serve to point up the disturbing fact that man is rapidly falling beneath, not moving beyond, his freedom and intrinsic worth by turning away from God. As Christians, it is our responsibility to assert our freedom by making responsible choices which are in tune with God's will and which evidence a sensitivity to the needs of our world. In so doing we move from beneath freedom and dignity to the significance of being fully human.

Francis Schaeffer has summarized the matter as follows: "What has happened to man? We must see him as one who has torn himself away both from the infinite-personal God who created him as finite but in His image, and from God's revelation to him. Made in God's image, man was made to be great, he was made to be beautiful and he was made to be creative in life and art. But his rebellion has led him into making himself into nothing but a machine."[5]

---

1. *B. F. Skinner,* Beyond Freedom and Dignity *(New York: Alfred A. Knopf, 1971), p. 200.*
2. *Francis A. Schaeffer,* Back to Freedom and Dignity *(Downers Grove, Ill.: InterVarsity Press, 1972), p. 47.*
3. *Skinner,* Beyond Freedom and Dignity, *p. 27.*
4. *Ibid., p. 201.*
5. *Schaeffer,* Back to Freedom and Dignity, *p. 48.*

A Psychiatrist's Reactions
to Skinner
by David F. Busby

I am not sure that B. F. Skinner deserves all the billing and attention we are giving him here. I say this with all due respect to his substantial contributions and to Dr. Under-wager's favorable comments (and I appreciate and agree substantially with what both he and Dr. Crabb have said). I do not mean to denigrate Skinner, but I am not really that impressed. On occasion I use his method of operant conditioning in my psychiatric practice and appreciatively so, I trust. But, while he is entitled to his "day in court," he has had quite a few of them, and I feel rather like saying, "So we have another endless repetition of one more erudite but truncated-by-his-atheistic-pre-supposition speakers, so what else is new?" I would hope that Christian psychologists and psychiatrists would have something a little more positive to offer than one more rehash of the Christian refutation of Skinner.

My "non-impressment" with Skinner is unmoved by Under-wager's praise; and it is not only unmoved but rather *enhanced* when I read in *Psychology Today* the following: (1) Skinner was named as "the social scientist whose work is most respected at Johns Hopkins" and (2) A Southern Methodist University poll named him "the only living scholar among the ten greatest in the history of psychology."

Nevertheless, because requested, I will give some of my own evaluation of Skinner. Dr. Harris, editorializing in *Psychology Today* (August, 1971), said, *"Beyond Freedom and Dignity* will outrage most people who read it." I was determined not to be. I was aware of a preconscious prejudice against Skinner, likely traceable to his atheism rather than his operant conditioning (which, as I said, I freely though cautiously use on occasion), but I attempted to override this prejudice, determining to be cool, calm and collected, and to give him an overly sympathetic hearing. At the onset, may I report, I *did* succeed in avoiding outrage, but I *could not* remain cool, calm and collected, for repeatedly the feeling pushed into my awareness that this poor man has much to offer but is misguided and truncated by what seems to me his sadly erroneous basic presuppositions. The last chapter of his book, by the way, entitled "What Is Man?" gives such presuppositions away completely.

BEHIND AND BENEATH FREEDOM AND DIGNITY
At this time, in a fashion somewhat characteristic of Freud, I shall attempt to trace a large part of Skinner's position to his childhood. Here, I think, it would be interesting and provocative to read a rather long excerpt from Harris:

Skinner's family was warm and stable, and much concerned about good behavior. "I was taught to fear God, the police, and what people would think," Skinner recalls, and he suspects that his reaction may have led him to try proving that people don't think at all. An old maid school teacher taught him English composition in the public school and Old Testament language and morals in the Presbyterian Sunday school. His father took him through the county jail to show him the punishment he would face if he were to develop the criminal mind. He was never whipped. Once when he used a bad word, his mother washed out his mouth with soap. Grandmother Skinner had him peer into the glowing coals of the parlor stove to gain a sense of hell.

Shortly after Skinner reached puberty, he had his one mystical experience. He lost his watch and, miserable and afraid to go home without it, peddled his bike along a creek to a shack. . . . [He reports], "suddenly it occurred to me that happiness and unhappiness must cancel out and that if I were unhappy now, I would necessarily be happy later. I was tremendously relieved. The principle came with the force of revelation. In a mood of intense exaltation, I started down along the creek. Halfway to the road, in a nest of dried grass beside the path, lay my watch. I have no explanation; I had certainly 'lost' it in town. I took this as a Sign." But within a year he had become the atheist he is today.

In college at Hamilton he tried to wreck the oratorical contest, commencement and righteous rituals. He used the student newspaper to attack the faculty, Phi Beta Kappa (he is a member) and other totems. His protest hit a deadly serious anger at triviality, and he poured the rage into short stories. . . .

Six months in Greenwich Village taught him what was wrong with being a writer. Since he had nothing important to say, writing was but pencil-craft. Ivan Pavlov's Conditioned Reflexes *and Bertrand Russell's* Philosophy—*mainly the section on J. B. Watson's behaviorism—offered a more convincing way to study behavior. So he went off to take his Ph.D. (1931) at Harvard's department of psychology.*

He taught at Minnesota for a while and then became chairman of psychology at Indiana (1945-1948) before he returned to Harvard.

BEYOND FREEDOM AND DIGNITY: AN ASSESSMENT

Now to specific comments about the work currently under assessment, *Beyond Freedom and Dignity.* On page 1, Skinner states, "Our [America's] strength is science and technology." That is the popular view and, at least in part, a valid assessment —that we in America see ourselves as technologically proficient and progressive. But whether that alleged fact overshadows and excludes any other strengths with which we might cope and shape our environment seems to me to depend on just who the "we" is; more specifically, whether "we" happens to be that portion of "us" who assess strength solely materialistically, or another portion of "us," perhaps not as small as some might think and certainly not limited to Christians, who, with a vision more holistic, would see strength in our country's religious heritage and in continuing such propensities. This religious tendency, incidentally, Skinner either ignores or attacks, depending on which seems to suit his purpose or mood. For example, Skinner quotes favorably Darlington's "Every new source from which man has increased his power on earth has been used to diminish the prospects of his successors." Even granting that religion as such has sometimes been misused and made a vehicle for man's diminishment of man, one wonders if it is naively idealistic to affirm that God is the *one* outstanding power source who *refuses* to be used for such diminishment even if he is rejected.

Next, I want to ask Skinner whether his autonomous free man of dignity created this terrible world we now live in. Is the culprit the *possession* of freedom and dignity or the *misperception* and *abuse* of freedom and dignity, a failure to enter with holy boldness into the freedom and dignity God offers to every man? Obviously, I am convinced it is the latter that has led to the mess that Skinner so adequately and aptly describes. On page 59, Skinner attributes the assassinations of the Kennedys and of Martin Luther King to the free concept of autonomous man derived from religion. That seems an interesting non sequitur to me.

I would like to share here briefly three ideas for which I am largely indebted to Mr. Ted Hsieh, a Chinese psychologist at Judson College near Chicago, who is doing his doctorate on operant conditioning. First, insofar as we might believe Skinner correct, he does effectively destroy humanism, idealism and the last vestige of modernism, anything that ever saw man as inherently good, and as freely and successfully ushering in his own golden-age utopia. Skinner says, "We're in bad shape if this is the best we can do." He seems to say that to seek some semi-benevolent dictator rather than to "go to Hell in a basket" by way of the free democratic society is the lesser of two evils.

Second, anybody who has tried to break a bad habit by sheer

will power, by turning over a new leaf, knows that Skinner is right when he demonstrates that in almost any contest between the rational conscious being and the unconscious, *one knows* who is going to win. Skinner seems to use unconsciously determined patterns in some presumably constructive way, leaving other people to continue to try to pump up the sagging ego which results from its "hero" of conscious rationality being soundly defeated.

And third, whereas Freudian determinism is often so societally abused as to, in effect, "overresponsibilize" mother and "irresponsibilize" child (even after he becomes an adult), it is interesting to note that Skinner's determinism hardly lends itself to such abuse. Rather it emphasizes (1) parental opportunity and (2) child-becoming-adult personal responsibility; and I say Amen to that. I confess, however, that I still do not quite grasp how he accomplishes this feat, that is, how he opts for determinism and "devolution," and yet hopes for and expects change (and for the better!). Dr. Lacy Hall pointed out to me that Isidore Cheins' *The Science of Behavior and the Image of Man* is billed as a "definitive corrective to Skinner," although it was written before *Beyond Freedom and Dignity* was released.

PROBLEMS OF MEDICAL PRACTICE

Leaving Skinner behind, I would like to share with you some of the problems of medical (psychiatric) practice. In my experience, doctors long ago quit struggling with the question of whether to play God and moved on to a concern about how to *better* play God. The decision to select one of five applicants for the kidney dialysis machine, difficult as it is, is often the least, if not the easiest, of the God-like decisions we are called upon to make. Consider these five examples:

1. Shock therapy (which I use in about 10% of my cases). What does the Scripture say about it, pro or con? Is the risk run and damage done, albeit temporary and small, justified by its potential but by no means certain benefit?

2. Hypnosis (which I have used in about 3% of my cases over the past twenty-seven years). What do the Scriptures say about this? Would you pray with a patient in a hypnotic trance or a post-hypnotic state? Incidentally, I might mention that medical hypnosis is a *cooperation* of wills, never the domination-submission of wills which is such a common misguided idea.

3. "Truth Serum" (which I use in about 5% of my cases). When and with whom should the results be shared? If the patient's own conscious mind cannot stand to accept the material directly from his unconscious, then who am I to unload the material on his conscious mind by telling him what he has said. Yet, if I do not, feeling it is for his good, what of the patient's right to know? And how may this patient's trust in me, one basic ingredient in the doctor/patient relationship, be affected, since he knows that I know something about him that he does not know?

4. Dreams. What is morally acceptable to dream about? Everything, because you cannot help it? Or only certain things, and if so, which ones? Is a dreamer's waking guilt feeling a reliable guide?

5. The less profound but common, everyday, equally complex decision as to which patient I see, on which day and in what order. Is it fair to determine this by what is called "the tyranny of the urgent" and hop from one to the other in the multi-daily (I assure you) crisis intervention? Or should choice be by other criteria than immediacy of need, even if that need could be determined in advance? And what are "other criteria" besides the limit of my capacity?

In mentioning these five items, I do not think I am complaining, for, as Harry Truman once said, "If you can't stand the heat, stay out of the kitchen." But I submit them as examples of God-like decisions doctors must make. I hope this does not sound arrogant (but if it does, so be it), but to me it seems obvious that God has chosen to use man as his instrument, albeit an often inefficient and not humble one.

The scientific practitioner's ethical decision must often

quickly be made by what might be called "flying by the seat of his hopefully-Christian pants!" This is not to say that it is impossible or not worthwhile to make a careful and *prayerful* analysis of the ingredients that go into such a decision, nor is it to justify unthinking impetuosity. For more than psychiatrists know that "fools rush in where angels fear to tread." I am sure I am not alone in leaning very heavily in my decisions every day on 1 Thessalonians 5:17 and Romans 12:12, which commend us to live constantly in an atmosphere of prayer, and on Romans 8:26-27, which teaches us that his Spirit knows what our needs are and speaks for us.

V

The New Image of Man

The New Image of Man
by Carl F.H. Henry

The notion of a new way of life and a new breed of humanity riddles the air. On all sides propagandists dangle before us the prospect of a new you or me. Nowhere is this possibility of transformed humanity projected with more enthusiasm than in frontier scientific circles, although science, to be sure, is not its only stamping ground. On every hand we sense an almost tangible atmosphere throbbing with zestful expectation and fanned at once by desperation and aspiration. The image of man is up for grabs today as it has not been since the Fall in the Garden of Eden and the indecisiveness of the Darwinian zoo.

A new breed of female and a new breed of male romp the pages of contemporary magazines. Women's Liberation calls for a new kind of woman. Even many of the clergy long for a new identity; some call for the Pope to lead the way. The unemployed battle past sobriquets of worthlessness and shiftlessness and demand that they not be demeaned as unworthy. Homosexuals call for equal rights to erase their age-old dismissal as non-humans. With the Pentagon draft near an end, some observers now foresee the emergence of a new class of centurion or professional soldier, with a resultant revival of ancient military virtues.

Social critics complain that the mass media accommodate this modern pursuit of a new image almost to the point of commercially exploiting all segments of society. Counter-cultural youth distrust the media and even elementary school children are skeptical of television commercials. Alienated blacks either aspire to a larger stake in the affluent society or, calling the purchasable new look an American economic seduction of the Negro by decadent white values, promote Afro alternatives instead.

Sensitive Christians shudder at the "ultimate image" guaranteed to owners of the latest car models and other credit-card possessions that outdo the Joneses, although similar expectations may have been nurtured by naive evangelistic assurances that Jesus gives financial success as surely as he forgives sins.

IMAGE: REALITY OR MASK?

In the Christian tradition image means reality; Christ is the image of God because he is essentially marked with the divine nature. The believer, in turn, is admonished to become conformed to the image of Christ. But for modern man image represents a mask, a veneer, the supreme hallucination that he can be essentially other than what he is. Image now promises an inversion of reality. Its mythological grip upon secular society has even nourished a lack of will to distinguish death and life, an indisposition grossly demonstrated in the way moderns paint up and display their dead as if they were alive and well.

Towering alongside the modern aspirations of image is a new concept of the good life. Fixed standards and external authority it considers a threat to the joy of being; God and his commandments and Christ and spiritual rebirth it therefore shuns as undesirable. This new notion of life at its best rejects evangelical faith not because the doctrines of creation or redemption or of a final resurrection are patently incredible but because such views are personally distasteful. The quasi-hedonistic approach emphasizes not merely that material sufficiency and bodily pleasure are essential to an authentically human life; it stresses rather that the essence of meaningful human existence is to be found in the present, more specifically, in this-worldly fullness and sensual delights. This earth-bound generation disowns Jesus of Nazareth as exemplar because his vocation involved forfeiting sexual pleasures and material indulgences, and especially because for him the serenity and security of life was to be found in God alone.

While alienated youth may repudiate commercialism and militarism, and even champion social justice, their infatuation with love, except for the Jesus-movement, is notably devoid of the first and great commandment. In these circles, no less than in the secular materialistic society they castigate, the Pauline phrase "haters of God" finds a snug fitting. Their infatuation with love is also noteworthy for its distortion of neighbor-love. To match their restyling of the good life, devotees of the modern mood have fashioned an experimental concept of love whose birth pangs are widespread syphilis and hepatitis.

Over against the secular Western man's sex-centered and thing-centered image—the two often abet each other—stands the political image of the ideal man nurtured by Chinese and Soviet communism. Here the ideal man is dedicated to world revolution, aggressively committed to the socio-political objectives projected by communist leaders and devoted whole-soul to the Party. The model man is a revolutionary figure hateful of the capitalist system and energetically engaged in implementing communist social patterns; the supernatural he repudiates as harmful myth and champions the totalitarian state as the final seat of authority. During the Chinese Cultural Revolution, Red Guards maligned Christian churches as the advocates of social injustice; Christians were demeaned as retrogressive parasites because they did not uncritically support communist politico-economic goals. In 1969 the communist paper *Red Flag* declared that building Christ's kingdom on earth is as incompatible with promoting communist ideals as are fire and water.

SCIENCE'S NEW MAN
If the communist vision of the new man represents a frontier perspective with which the twentieth century must actively cope, no less does the emerging scientific postulation of a new

man. Advances in genetic mutation have spawned the hope that, by eliminating unwelcome features and incorporating desirable traits, laboratory scientists might breed an archetypal man that could be cloned or artifically reproduced. Venturesome experimentalists speak of a new and superior man—a man with built-in spare parts or with extra fingers to expedite mechanical manipulations or perhaps even a rear-view eye serviceable to detective and criminal alike. But as more people use tranquilizers, and take drugs to expand their mind or change their personality, the question becomes more and more urgent just what kind of person is to be considered ideally human.

Into whose image, for example, are all Americans to be cloned? Billy Graham's? Pat Nixon's? William Buckley's? Sammy Davis Jr.'s? Martha Mitchell's? George McGovern's? Hitler and the Nazis considered Jews to be a species of humanity inferior to Nordic types, and so they ventured to preserve the one and to exterminate the other. Is it conceivable that in a secular scientistic society those who believe in the supernatural will be labeled retrogressive and therefore marked for liquidation in some modern experimental Colosseum? Feuerbach's followers already swell the ranks of communists, humanists and atheists in contending that belief in God discourages human moral development and world-engagement since to believe in God is also to believe that the good will prevail even without man's energetic striving. It is the tragic irony of human existence, however, that when fallen man seeks to elevate himself to superhumanity, as if he were himself God and the creator of his cosmic destiny, he soon succeeds only in transforming himself into an iniquitous monster who grandiosely rationalizes the aberrations he elevates as sacred and moral. Christ can forgive sinners, but the false gods are much more difficult to forgive.

Central to the current conflict over the ideal image of man is the contemporary uncertainty about who or what man really is. This bewilderment follows hard on the recent modern uncertainty about God. Concepts of the nature of man inevitably reveal the values man considers ultimately worthy of his worship and wages. It has not yet dawned on contemporaries that their creative postulation of a novel man, if consistently ventured, must involve a total severance with man as Christianity has known him—man destined to an afterlife, man ideally imaged in Jesus of Nazareth, man who owes his existence to a divine creator and preserver. The man who denies transcendent creation, destiny or abiding meaning and worth must eventually realize that he is nothing but haphazardly animated dust that has no permanent importance; each day moves him but closer to the crematory as the finality of his being. His individual concern for social justice or for interpersonal love then has neither cosmic basis nor support, and his struggle for security occurs on a planet begotten of an unpredictable explosion and dependent on some kind of galactic lottery.

CHRISTIANITY'S OFFER
The vision of a new image and a new life, of the new birth through which one enters the kingdom of God, is of course integral to evangelical Christianity. If proffers to every man the prospect of becoming a new creature for whom "there is a new world; the old order has gone, and a new order has already begun" (2 Cor. 5:17, NEB). Only broken fragments of this biblical heritage survived in the Protestant modernist emphasis on an integrated personality in which Jesus as example, replacing Jesus as the divine Mediator, achieves the spiritual unification of the discordant self. However much more evangelical Christianity has preserved of the supernatural biblical realities neglected by modern religious theory, the issue forced upon the Christian community today gives little more comfort to regenerate Christians than to the victims of a backslidden theology. Sad to say, even pious followers of Christ are blameworthy for much of the present uncertainty over the biblical image of man.

This cultural culpability is not due simply to the intractableness of even regenerate human nature. Christianity has from the first insisted that the believer, while given a new power for righteousness in the Holy Spirit, will experience growing pains in this life of grace; sinless glorification is a condition reserved for the life to come. Western man in his age of highest spiritual commitments and moral concerns saw in Jesus Christ the image of the perfect man. Jesus enfleshed the will of God as the Second Adam, and by his perfect manhood and atoning death opened a new way to life for his trusting followers. The Spirit dynamically conforms the redeemed man to Christ's ethical likeness, but only in the life to come are the godly cloned completely to his righteous image.

More distressing is the fact that what many Christians exhibit as the life of obedient sonship to God actually eclipses facets of human experience that the contemporary man considers indispensably integral to ethical humanity. Many evangelical Christians pass over aspects of social and cultural concern, and dimensions of personal existence, as if the believer proceeds all at once from the altar rail, or the new birth, to his final destiny in another world.

Just as the apostle Paul had to remind certain enthusiasts at Thessalonica that the resurrection was still future and had not yet occurred, so a responsible biblical theology must today remind evangelical Christians that what new life in Christ implies must be translated into a new image of man, an image that can confront the contemporary alternatives concerned with man's three-score years and ten. It was while Lazarus lay dead and prior to his revivification that Jesus reminded Mary and Martha, "I *am* the resurrection and the life." What does the life and resurrection that Christ *now is* imply for the current debate over the image of man?

Certainly in view of Christ's redemptive vocation Christian ethics must not be oversimplified into an imitation of Jesus, which the New Testament in any event forecloses as a basis of salvation. His self-emptying and obedient sonship nonetheless remain the model of sanctification for all who are justified by faith in Him (see Gal. 4:19; Phil. 2:5). The relationship between the ideal Christian image and Jesus is as inviolable as is the connection between man's salvation (Rom. 5:10) and the correlation of his final destiny (1 Jn. 3:2) with Christ's holy likeness. Apostolic literature clearly spells out what evangelical obedience to God's revealed will principally requires of the Christian in the world in matters of the state and society and in family relationships.

MAN'S IDEAL IMAGE IN THE SEVENTIES
Let me offer some suggestions as to what the New Testament implies for man's ideal image in the 1970s.

1. The communist world, and humanists and atheistic capitalists as well, need to be reminded that social justice and political righteousness are irreducible demands of the Living God. That message needs to be heard no less urgently in the noncommunist world, even where state and church seem to be cronies. It is not enough simply to imply that the Living God joins in man's cry for social and economic justice, as if Yahweh had recently taken graduate studies in the writings of Marx and Sartre. God himself is the stipulator of the public righteousness he requires, a fact that the ancient prophets, long before the modern rebirth of social concern, expressed in articulate commandments. Those commandments are addressed to Marxists and existentialists and capitalists alike.

Any call for socio-economic-political justice that calls also for the rejection of God and the supernatural is a phony; by eclipsing God and his will such a formulation can substitute totalitarianism or free enterprise or human subjectivity and redefine justice according to man's preferences. This loss of the category of transcendent justice is, in fact, one of the self-destructive features of contemporary ethical concern. Yet more is needed than a proclamation of God's commandments above the history of our times as an ideal suspended irrelevantly on Cloud Seven. Evangelical Christians are called to historical and political engagement; they are to enunciate the perfect will of God, support the best available options, arouse both public indignation and aspiration, and publicly demonstrate in their own community of the committed what the righteousness of God implies for personal as well as social relationships.

2. Evangelical Christians probably raise even less doubt about the propriety of material ambitions than they do about the indispensability of social justice; indeed, the Jesus Movement faults many evangelicals for being no less given over to an American two-car materialistic philosophy than are non-evangelicals. What Christianity has to say to the materialistic mentality of our age must not be left to alienated youth. For it is just as wrong to oversimplify the itinerant ministry of Jesus into a principle of portable possessions as to equate security and serenity with earthly abundance. Scripture teaches that all possessions—whether few or many—are a responsible stewardship, that those with many are privileged and obliged to bless those with few, that God looks with compassion on the poor and apprehension on the rich. No less must it be said, however, with such power that modern man imagines termites invading his comfortable castles, that to set one's heart on material things is to eclipse the dignity and destiny of man.

3. Evangelical Christians will have to say much more with regard to sex. True and pointed as their verdict is that modern man has millennial expectations from sex and is therefore foredoomed to frustration, Christians should offer perceptive direction in this realm of relationships as well. There is no doubt that as intercourse has come more free and easy, so love has become more elusive. Yet modern man is not wholly wrong in regarding much of what in the past was called Christian sexual ethics to be merely prudish legalism that had no legitimate basis in human welfare and even eroded it. Nor is he now impressed by what love means among many today who elevate *agape* to front-row prominence; how much remains to be learned about ideal sexuality is clear from the fact that even the counseling sessions of the clergy today revolve mainly around problems of sex.

While in the life to come there will be no "giving in marriage," in the present life sex and marriage are God's normative purposes for mankind. In view of contemporary man's exaggerated expectations from sex, theology has a responsibility for speaking relevantly concerning its rightful role. Human sexuality is a gift of God, respectable and honorable. To be sure, any reader of the New Testament is aware that some of its severest warnings are against sexual immorality. The Bible associates intercourse exclusively with marriage and includes in adultery even the lustful look, a popular preoccupation of the modern Western world. The Bible, however, neither limits marital intercourse solely to procreation nor premarital love to amorphous nonsexuality.

The penalty for adding the traditions of man to what God commands or forbids inevitably includes an excessive future reaction; human nature itself, although unregenerate, may reach out for what is not really contrary to ideal human expression, and men may divest themselves of God in repudiating what others have artificially associated with him. An authentically evangelical exposition of ideal sexual morality is indispensable and imperative for our times.

4. As far as science and the ideal man is concerned, the Christian finds the problems of medical ethics less serious when science functions to restore what from the standpoint of creation may be considered physically normal. Dark doubts arise, however, when genetic experimentalists talk about a new and superior man. Modern thought has all but dumped the fact that life is a gift, a gift of God; for that reason it resists the promise of new life as well as a divine gift.

The choices that man increasingly faces in the bewildering twentieth century are nothing less than ultimate and final. The alternatives are either the redemption of man or the manipulation of man. If the present scientific age does indeed overpower and manipulate man, it will but move up the inflexible inevitability of hell from the future life to come to this present one. Humanists who, in deference to an evolutionary view of ethics, have already tried to outmode the moral image of Jesus, have succeeded neither in validating any permanent moral alternatives or in eclipsing the ethical supremacy of Jesus the Nazarene. It remains true today as in Eden that he who shuns the word and image of God abandons himself to the lie and image of Satan.

Already at man's creation God declared that his image was to be set in man (Gen. 1:26; 9:6) and not, as the Decalogue disallows, in graven stone or mere cosmic dust (Ex. 20:4). Yet future, in that Kingdom where divine sonship and love and justice universally prevail, lies the redeemed man's destiny of being fully conformed to the image enfleshed in Jesus of Nazareth. In the interim, his opportunity and responsibility are to reflect that image to a society whose concept and practice of love tend to be amoral, whose exercise of justice caters to class interest and for whom the phrase *divine sonship* has become foreign and unintelligible.

The regenerate Christian must therefore radiate a burnished image that reflects the passion of the ancient prophets for public righteousness no less than for personal holiness; show a stewardship of substance impressing both disciples and doubters that the carpets and cars in our own castles and not simply the cattle on a thousand hills are truly the Lord's; demonstrate marital love as a courtship that the world cannot improve, that death alone can undo and eternity alone enhance; and live life not as a hopeless debt but as a divine gift whose horizons include the wonder of creation, redemption and resurrection. Any lesser image is likely now to seem so sheer that Christians appear as nude as the rest of the human race.

Participants

Participants in an invitational conference sponsored by the Institute for Advanced Christian Studies in An.ı Arbor, Michigan, in October, 1972: "The Scientist and Ethical Decision"

Hanley Abramson, Ph.D., Assistant Professor of Pharmaceutical Chemistry, Wayne State University.

V. Elving Anderson, Ph.D., Professor of Genetics and Cell Biology, and Assistant Director, Dight Institute of Human Genetics, University of Minnesota.

David F. Busby, M.D., Professor of Pastoral Psychology, Trinity Evangelical Divinity School, and practicing psychiatrist.

J. Frank Cassel, M.A., Ph.D., Professor of Zoology, North Dakota State University.

Lawrence J. Crabb, Jr., Ph.D., Director of Psychological Counseling Center, Florida Atlantic University, and clinical psychologist.

Charles Hatfield, Ph.D., Professor of Mathematics, University of Missouri, Rolla.

Walter R. Hearn, B.A., Ph.D., Visiting Associate Professor of Biochemistry, University of California, Berkeley.

Carl F. H. Henry, Ph.D., Editor at Large, *Christianity Today,* and Professor at Large, Eastern Baptist Theological Seminary.

John A. McIntyre, B.S., M.A., Ph.D., Professor of Physics, Texas A&M University.

Ronald H. Nash, A.B., M.A., Ph.D., Professor of Philosophy, and Head, Department of Philosophy and Religion, Western Kentucky University.

Stanley Obitts, Ph.D., Professor of Philosophy, Westmont College.

Kenneth L. Pike, Ph.D., Professor of Linguistics, University of Michigan.

Henry Stob, A.B., B.D., Th.M., Ph.D., Professor of Christian Ethics, Calvin Theological Seminary.

Ralph C. Underwager, Jr., Ph.D., Department of Psychology, St. Olaf College, and certified psychologist.